The New Science of Skin and Scuba Diving

A Project of the Council
for National Co-operation in Aquatics

Editorial Committee

BERNARD E. EMPLETON, CHAIRMAN

EDWARD H. LANPHIER, M.D.

JAMES E. YOUNG

LOYAL G. GOFF

THE NEW SCIENCE OF
SKIN AND SCUBA DIVING

Third Revised Edition

Illustrations by ANDRE ECUYER

ASSOCIATION PRESS · NEW YORK

FOREWORD

Far-ranging developments in the use of scuba as a tool for scientists engaged in underwater research mark the period since CNCA's early publishing venture, the widely accepted *Science of Skin and Scuba Diving*, published in 1957.

The size of areas now open to scuba divers along the continental shelves of the earth are estimated to approximate a land mass the size of North America. Oceanography is rapidly developing into a mature science. Recent heavy financial appropriations by our government for research and exploration under water are impressive evidence of the interest that our scientists and leaders share in the vast, unexplored regions beneath the seas. The discovery of mineral deposits to replace our gutted surface mines, the possibility of submarine gardens to feed the teeming populations of the earth, the opportunities for archaeological research into man's distant past—all hold challenge sufficient to test the boldest spirits and quicken our most inventive minds.

This book is dedicated to these great adventures. We believe they are approached through the gateway of sound fundamentals in theory and technique.

GLADYS BROWN
Chairman
Council for National Co-operation in Aquatics

ABOUT THE CNCA

Purpose

The purpose of the Council for National Co-operation in Aquatics (CNCA) is to provide a setting in which official representatives from *national organizations* conducting and/or promoting aquatic activities can come together to:

    (1) report on individual agency programs, plans, and projects

    (2) share and discuss common problems

    (3) plan ways of working together on agreed-upon projects

    (4) help advance the broad field of aquatics

It is the hope that this planning and working together on appropriate and well-defined tasks will bring about a greater understanding among agencies and make it possible to serve a larger number of people more effectively. Such cooperative efforts, added to the independent work carried on continuously by the various agencies, should creatively advance the entire field of aquatics.

Membership

Participation on the CNCA Board of Directors shall be of two types:

    Agency members: Representatives from national organizations that have an interest in aquatics.

    Selected Consultants: Persons who have particular abilities or interest in aquatics or closely related fields.

Participating national groups are:

    Amateur Athletic Union of the United States (AAU)

    American Association for Health, Physical Education, and Recreation (AAHPER)

    —General representation (staff)

    —Division for Girls' and Women's Sports (DGWS)

    American Camping Association (ACA)

American National Red Cross (ARC)
American Park and Recreation Society (APRS)
American Public Health Association (APHA)
American Swimming Coaches Association (ASCA)
Athletic Institute, Inc. (AI)
Boy Scouts of America (BSA)
Boys' Clubs of America (BCA)
Camp Fire Girls, Inc. (CFG)
National Association of Intercollegiate Athletics (NAIA)
National Association of Underwater Instructors (NAUI)
National Board of the Young Women's Christian Association (YWCA)
National Collegiate Athletic Association (NCAA)
National Council of Young Men's Christian Associations (YMCA)
  —General Representation (staff)
  —National Operating Council on Aquatics
National Federation of State High School Athletic Associations
    (NFSHSAA)
National Jewish Welfare Board (JWB)
National Recreation and Park Association (NRPA)
National Safety Council (NSC)
National Surf Lifesaving Association of America (NSLSAA)
National Swimming Pool Institute (NSPI)
President's Council on Physical Fitness and Sports (PCPFS)
Underwater Society of America (USA)
United States Office of Education (USOE)
United States Power Squadrons (USPS)
United States Public Health Service (USPHS)
Women's National Aquatic Forum (WNAF)

Additional information concerning the CNCA can be obtained by writing
to the National Offices of the member organizations or to 51 Clifford Avenue,
Pelham, N.Y. 10803.

HISTORICAL NOTE

The Council for National Co-operation in Aquatics sincerely acknowledges the work of the many contributors to *The New Science of Skin and Scuba Diving*.

The history of this book and its predecessor, *The Science of Skin and Scuba Diving*, is an interesting and encouraging one because it is an example of what can be done when individuals and organizations pool their resources in the interest of a common objective.

The initial momentum for the project was generated by the stimulating work of a number of skin and scuba diving enthusiasts who met as a working group during the Fourth Annual Meeting of the CNCA at Yale University, New Haven, Connecticut, in the fall of 1954. The findings of the group, with its recommendations, convinced the CNCA that additional attention should be given to this fast-growing activity. After careful consideration of the needs in this field the executive committee recommended that a handbook on skin and scuba diving be written. It was further recommended that the handbook reflect the considered opinions of experienced divers from all sections of the country. The Skin and Scuba Diving Committee of the CNCA was charged with the responsibility of the handbook, and a letter outlining the purposes of the book and containing a specific request for their assistance was directed to some twenty outstanding divers. The response was encouraging, and the project was under way.

Rough drafts of most of the chapters were ready for review at the 1955 meeting of the CNCA. Many excellent suggestions were received, and the authors were asked to incorporate them in the final draft. The completed manuscripts were again reviewed by the committee under the able leadership of Bernard E. Empleton, then Director of Physical Education, Central YMCA, Washington, D.C.

Those of us who have been fortunate enough to observe the work of the committee and the contributors, are fully aware of the sacrifices that were made in order that this book could be completed. The CNCA is deeply appreciative of their tremendous efforts, and it is our sincere hope that these efforts will contribute to safety and therefore increased enjoyment of skin and scuba divers wherever they may dive.

RICHARD L. BROWN
Former Chairman
Council for National Co-operation in Aquatics

CONTENTS

LIST OF ILLUSTRATIONS

INTRODUCTION

Once again a major revision of *The New Science of Skin and Scuba Diving* has been undertaken. For a decade, this text has been the training manual for instruction courses taught by the YMCA, Boy Scouts, schools and colleges, and diving groups across the United States and for many divers the world over. Seven printings and the sale of a quarter million copies testifies to the soundness of the work which was sponsored by the Council for National Co-operation in Aquatics in 1954.

Time and improved techniques in both teaching and equipment dictate the changes recorded herein. A new focus of attention has been given the vast reaches of "inner space." Scientists can no longer remain in remote university laboratories and fully appreciate the vast areas of knowledge being unlocked in the seas of the world. Scuba provides a tool for the scientist, sportsman, hobbyist, and lawman.

Over the past ten years, great strides have been made in teaching the use of scuba. New equipment has been developed and still newer equipment is about to be made available in the marketplace.

The government has begun to insist on safe standards for breathing air. International conclaves of diving leaders have considered such items as minimum qualifications for divers, international safety standards, exchange of information regarding equipment and the possibility of a body of diving law.

Youth continues to be lured by the sea frontier in a world where physical frontiers are rapidly vanishing.

Since *The Science of Skin and Scuba Diving* was published in 1957 as the only comprehensive text for the civilian sport diver, several national standard courses have been developed. The YMCA was first, followed by NAUI (National Association of Underwater Instructors). The Boy Scouts of America adopted the YMCA course early and later that of NAUI. The text for these courses has been *The Science of Skin and Scuba Diving*.

The diving fraternity has had a vested interest in this work from the beginning. From hundreds of courses and seminars have come valuable ideas which have found their way into revisions. It is not possible to fully acknowledge or adequately identify the contributions of the many divers who shared their love for diving and concern for safety and who are very much a part of this book.

It is possible to acknowledge the very direct contributions of the smaller group who, through specific assignments are represented here. They are: Edward H. Lanphier, M.D., State University of New York at Buffalo, Department of Physiology, School of Medicine; Mr. Loyal Goff, National Aeronautics and Space Administration, Washington, D.C.; Captain James T. Wren, Army Ordnance Disposal, formerly Technical Adviser to the Underwater Panel, National Academy of Science, Washington, D.C.; Mr. Wallace Hagerhorst, Instructor at George Washington University, Washington, D.C.; Mr. E. R. Cross, Master Diver, writer, lecturer, and teacher of scuba and deep-sea rig diving; William T. Burns, M.D., Long Beach, California; Mr. Gilbert Abbe, Director, Medical Gas Division of the Southern Oxygen Company, Washington, D.C.; Mr. Richard Morris, Water Safety Director, Red Cross, West Palm Beach, Florida; Mr. James E. Young, formerly White House Police Training Division and First Chairman of the National YMCA Skin and Scuba Diving Committee; Mr. Fred Schwankovsky, former Director of Lifesaving and Water Safety, Long Beach, California; and Mr. John Moloney, present National Chairman of the YMCA Skin and Scuba Diving Program.

The interest of manufacturers who have helped from the beginning is gratefully acknowledged. They are: U.S. Divers; Northill Garrett Corporation; The Southern Oxygen Company of Washington, D.C.; and Adolf Kiefer Company of Chicago, Illinois.

For the improved schematic diagrams of regulators and explanatory text a special note of appreciation to U.S. Divers for permission to use these. Appreciation to the United States Government and in particular the United States Navy for permission to print the diving tables.

Dr. Lanphier has very carefully revised the material on medical aspects of diving. As a figure of international importance in diving research he continues to renew this text with the latest medical information. Loyal Goff, in collaboration with John Moloney, has approached the physics of diving with a keen sense of the need for simplifying a complex topic. James Young, widely recognized for his teaching skill has consolidated the experience of many years and many teachers into a greatly improved rendering.

The results of the efforts of these men, backed by many others, is presented here as the renewal of a text by and for divers wherever they be.

The time and energies of all contributors are given freely in the public interest.

BERNARD E. EMPLETON
Chairman
Editorial Committee

1

BASIC REQUIREMENTS FOR SKIN AND SCUBA DIVING

With or without scuba, diving and underwater swimming make unusual demands on the participant both physically and psychologically. A person will run more than ordinary risks in this kind of activity if he has certain physical defects, if he is not in good general physical condition and "fitness," or if he tends toward emotional instability. If he does not mind accepting the risk, this might be considered his own business. However, he should not expect an organization which sponsors training or other activities in the sports to welcome him with open arms. Sponsorship involves concern (and sometimes some actual responsibility) for an individual's own safety, and instructors and fellow participants also deserve consideration. Both physical condition and swimming ability are important.

Swimming Ability and Watermanship

1. Tread water, feet only, 3 minutes.
2. Swim 300 yards without fins.
3. Tow an inert swimmer 40 yards without fins.
4. Stay afloat 15 minutes without accessories.
5. Swim under water 15 yards without fins—without pushoff.

These requirements are not difficult, but they do indicate a degree of watermanship which would enable an individual in difficulty to help himself without the aid of specialized gear.

Physical Status

A person who gets into trouble in water always endangers his companions to some degree, sometimes very seriously. For the candidate's own good as well as for this reason, most organizations concerned with underwater activities set up some kind of physical standards and insist that each prospective participant be examined by a doctor. Many of them also make an effort to size up whether the candidate is "in shape" or not, either through special fitness tests or in the course of checking his swimming ability. They also remain alert for evidence of psychological difficulties in the course of both testing and training.

From the doctor's standpoint, evaluating a person's fitness for diving, and deciding just where to draw the line on minor or questionable defects is not an entirely simple matter. Most physicians have had little direct experience with diving problems, and even the best set of "specs" is bound to leave much to the doctor's judgment. There are also important matters which he may have a hard time evaluating unless he has known the candidate for a long time. Episodes in a prospective diver's medical history and factors like psychiatric problems can easily remain undisclosed in a routine examination, and a doctor should not be blamed when such things slip by. The candidate himself, if he is willing to be honest, can help the doctor very much and may be able to do a good part of the "sizing up" job himself. (In the process, he may even spontaneously come to the conclusion that diving is not for him.)

Partly with such possibilities in mind, as well as to save the doctor's time, the suggested medical history and examination forms included in this chapter have a "do it yourself" section and include useful notes for the candidate as well as for the doctor.

Medical History and Examination Forms

TO THE APPLICANT:

You have requested training in an activity which makes considerable demands on your physical condition. Diving with certain defects amounts to asking for trouble—not only for you but for anybody who has to come to your aid if you get into difficulties in the water. For these reasons, the CNCA insists that you have a doctor's OK on your fitness for diving.

You are asked to fill out the Medical History form mainly to save the doctor's time. Not all the questions have a direct bearing on your fitness for diving. Some have to do with medical problems which should be looked into whether they concern diving or not. All are questions the doctor would ask you if he had time.

In many instances, your answers to the questions are more important in determining your fitness than what the doctor can see, hear, or feel when he examines you. Obviously, you must give accurate information, or the whole process becomes a waste of time. The forms will be kept in confidence. However, if you feel that any question amounts to an invasion of your privacy, you may omit the answer *provided that you discuss the matter with the doctor* and that he indicates that you have done so.

If the doctor concludes that diving would involve undue risk for you, remember that he is concerned only with your well-being and safety. Respect his advice.

MEDICAL HISTORY

Name: _____ Age: _____ yrs. Sex: _____

Address: _____ Telephone: _____

Height: _____ inches   Weight: _____ pounds

(If answers to the following questions require explanation, use the space labeled "Remarks," giving the number of the question.)

1. Have you had previous experience in diving? Yes__ No__ Have you done any flying? Yes__ No__ If so, did you often have trouble equalizing pressure in your ears or sinuses? Yes__ No__ Can you go to the bottom of a swimming pool without having discomfort in ears or sinuses? Yes__ No__

2. Do you participate regularly in active sports? Yes__ No__ If so, specify what sport(s). If not, indicate what exercise you normally obtain. _____
   _____

3. Have you ever been rejected for service or employment for medical reasons? Yes__ No__ *(If "Yes," explain in remarks or discuss with doctor.)*

4. When was your last physical examination? Month_____ Year_____

5. When was your last chest X ray? Month_____ Year_____

6. Have you ever had an electrocardiogram? Yes__ No__ An electroencephalogram (brain wave study)? Yes__ No__

(Check the blank if you have, or ever have had, any of the following. Explain under "Remarks," giving dates and other pertinent information; or discuss with the doctor).

7. Frequent colds or sore throat __
8. Hay fever or sinus trouble __
9. Trouble breathing through nose (other than during colds) __
10. Painful or running ear, mastoid trouble, broken eardrum __
11. Asthma or shortness of breath after moderate exercise __
12. Chest pain or persistent cough __
13. Spells of fast, irregular, or pounding heartbeat __
14. High or low blood pressure __
15. Any kind of "heart trouble" __
16. Frequent upset stomach, heartburn, or indigestion; peptic ulcer __
17. Frequent diarrhea. Blood in stools __
18. Belly or back ache lasting more than a day or two __
19. Kidney or bladder disease; blood, sugar, or albumin in urine __

20. Syphilis or gonorrhea __
21. Broken bone, serious sprain or strain, dislocated joint __
22. Rheumatism, arthritis, or other joint trouble __
23. Severe or frequent headaches __
24. Head injury causing unconsciousness __
25. Dizzy spells, fainting spells, or fits __
26. Trouble sleeping, frequent nightmares, or sleepwalking __
27. Nervous breakdown or periods of marked depression __
28. Dislike for closed-in spaces, large open places, or high places __
29. Any neurological condition __
30. Train, sea, or air sickness __
31. Alcoholism, or any drug or narcotic habit (including regular use of sleeping pills, benzedrine, etc.) __

32. Recent gain or loss of weight or appetite   ___
33. Jaundice or hepatitis   ___
34. Tuberculosis   ___
35. Diabetes   ___

36. Rheumatic fever   ___
37. Any serious accident, injury, or illness not mentioned above *(Describe under "Remarks," giving dates.)*   ___

REMARKS

_____

_____

_____

_____

_____

I certify that I have not withheld any information and that the above is accurate to the best of my knowledge.

Signature:_____

MEDICAL EXAMINATION OF DIVERS

TO THE PHYSICIAN:

The bearer requests evaluation of his fitness for *diving with breathing apparatus.* He has completed a medical history form (1) that should assist you. Besides assessment of his history, he requires a good general physical examination. Attention to psychiatric status is also indicated. Other procedures are at your discretion (*see below*).

Please bear in mind that diving involves a number of unusual medical considerations (2, 3). The main ones can be summarized as follows:

1. Diving involves *heavy exertion.* (A diver must be in good general health, be free of cardiovascular and respiratory disease, and have good exercise tolerance.)

2. All body air spaces must *equalize pressure* readily. (*Ear* and *sinus* pathology may impair equalization or be aggravated by pressure. Obstructive *lung* disease may cause catastrophic accidents on ascent.)

3. Even momentary *impairment of consciousness* underwater may result in death. (A diver must not be subject to syncope, epileptic episodes, diabetic problems, or the like.)

4. Lack of *emotional stability* seriously endangers not only the diver but also his companions. (Evidence of neurotic trends, recklessness, accident-proneness, panicky behavior, or questionable motivation for diving should be evaluated.)

SUGGESTED ADDITIONAL PROCEDURES:

(at physician's discretion)
> *Routine:* Chest film (if none within one year), urinalysis, wbc, hematocrit.
> *Divers over 40:* Electrocardiogram with step test.
> *Questionable respiratory status:* Lung volumes, timed vital capacity.

INOCULATIONS:

Divers often enter polluted water and are subject to injuries requiring anti-tetanus treatment. It is strongly advisable to keep all routine immunizations up to date. (Tetanus, typhoid, diphtheria, smallpox, poliomyelitis.)

REFERENCES:

(1) *The New Science of Skin and Scuba Diving.* New York: Association Press, 1967.
(2) Lanphier, E. H. "Medical Progress: Diving Medicine," *New Eng. J. Med.,* 256 (Jan. 17, 1957), 120–30.
(3) Duffner, G. J. "Scuba Diving Injuries, Predisposing Causes and Prevention," *J. Am. Med. Assn.,* 175 (Feb. 4, 1961), 375–78.

- -

(Please detach and return to examinee)

IMPRESSION

I have examined _____ and reached the following conclusion concerning his fitness for diving:

_____ *Approval.* (I find no defects that I consider incompatible with diving.)

_____ *Conditional approval.* (I do not consider diving in examinee's best interests but find no defects that present marked risk.)

_____ *Disapproval.* (Examinee has defects that I believe constitute unacceptable hazards to his health and safety in diving.)

The following conditions should be made known to any physician who treats this person for a diving accident (include medical conditions, drug allergies, etc.):

_____

_____

_____

Signature _____ M.D.

Address _____

Date _____

NOTE: A report form of this kind is available from Association Press.

The following paragraphs, extracted from an article by Dr. E. H. Lanphier ("Medical Progress: Diving Medicine," *N. Eng. J. Med.,* Jan. 17, 1957), may assist you in evaluating the applicant:

"One of the primary considerations is that diving involves *heavy exertion.* Even if a man does not intend to engage in spearfishing or other activities which are obviously demanding, he will sooner or later find himself in situations which tax his strength and endurance. Even the best breathing apparatus increases the work of breathing, and this adds to the problem of exertion under water. Lifting and carrying the heavy equipment on dry land is also hard work. The necessity for *freedom from cardiovascular and respiratory disease* is evident. Individuals who are sound but sedentary should be encouraged to improve their *exercise tolerance* gradually by other means before taking up diving. The influence of exertion on conditions such as diabetes should be considered carefully. It is not reasonable to apply a fixed age limit to sport divers, but *men over 40 deserve special scrutiny.*

"An absolute physical requirement for diving is the *ability of the middle ear and sinuses to equalize pressure changes.* The Navy applies a standard 'pressure test' in a recompression chamber to assess this ability since usual methods of examination have insufficient predictive value unless obvious pathology is present. However, even going to the bottom of a swimming pool will generally tell a man whether his Eustachian tubes and sinus ostia will transmit air readily or not. In the case of middle ear equalization, part of the problem is learning the technique of 'popping your ears.' Presence of *otitis* or *sinusitis* is a definite contraindication for diving, even in a man who can normally equalize pressure. A history of disorders of this sort suggests that diving is unwise; but as in the case of frequent colds or allergic rhinitis, prohibition of diving is not invariably justified. Here, much depends on the individual's common sense and ability to forego diving if he has trouble. A *perforated tympanic membrane* should rule out diving because of the near-certainty of water entering the middle ear. The use of ear plugs presents no solution to any of these problems and is, in fact, strongly contraindicated.

"Any organic *neurological disorder*, or a history of *epileptic episodes* or *losses of consciousness* from any cause, makes diving highly inadvisable. A more difficult problem for the physician to evaluate and handle adroitly arises in the *psychiatric* area. The *motivation* and *general attitude* of some aspirants make safe diving unlikely from the outset; and those individuals who tend to panic in emergencies may well find occasion for doing so in diving. *Recklessness* or *emotional instability* in a diver is a serious liability for his companions as well as for himself."

2

PHYSICS AS RELATED TO DIVING

All the new experiences, both pleasant and unpleasant, encountered in the sport of self-contained diving stem directly from the great differences in the physical properties and characteristics which exist between air and water environments. The differences most apparent are: the increased density and viscosity of the water, which make for almost complete freedom of movement in three dimensions but restrict the speed of movement; differences in acoustic and optical properties, which make underwater communication more difficult and alter the appearance of objects as to size, color, and distance; and the higher heat capacity of water, which places a greater drain on the heat stores of the body. Not so apparent, but of equal or greater significance, are the effects of pressure on the air being breathed at depth and the resulting physiologic effects.

These are some of the things that will be taken up in this chapter. Though the beginner may feel that some of the detail is excessive, it is certain that a reasonable understanding of these phenomena will help to increase the pleasures and reduce the hazards to be encountered in diving.

Matter and Some of Its Properties

Matter is defined as anything that occupies space and has weight. By definition then it includes everything outside an absolute vacuum or void. Matter may exist in one or more of three fundamental states: solid, liquid, or gas. Since a diver uses solid equipment and breathes a gas while immersed in a liquid, he is directly concerned with at least some of the basic characteristics of all. Temperature and pressure are probably the most important factors with which sport divers are concerned, and also the ones that have the most readily observed effects. They will therefore be taken up first and in the greatest detail. The diver who wishes to practice complicated or technical activities underwater must consult more advanced references.

TEMPERATURE

Matter is found in one or more of the three states—solid, liquid, or gas—depending upon the temperature. Water, for example, is a solid below 32° F., or 0° C. (the freezing point), a liquid at intermediate temperatures, and a gas (steam) at higher temperatures (above 212° F. or 100° C.). A certain amount of water is nearly always present in the air although it is not visible as steam.

The two notations "° F." and "° C." represent "degrees Fahrenheit" and "degrees Centigrade," respectively. The Fahrenheit scale is the one commonly used in the United States while the Centigrade scale is the one used in Europe and most of the rest of the world. Still another scale is the Kelvin, or Absolute, scale. From the figures given above, it can be seen that there are 180 Fahrenheit degrees between the boiling and the freezing points of water (32–212) while on the Centigrade scale there are 100 degrees (0–100). On the Kelvin scale the temperature change for each degree is identical to that for the Centigrade scale, but 273°A. (Absolute) is the same as 0° Centigrade. The relationship between these three scales is shown by the following conversion calculations:

EXAMPLES OF CONVERTING ONE TEMPERATURE SCALE TO ANOTHER*

1. Convert 20° Centigrade to Fahrenheit

$$9/5 \ C° + 32° = F°$$
$$(9/5 \times 20°) + 32° =$$
$$(9 \times 4°) + 32° =$$
$$36° + 32° =$$
Then 20° C = 68° F

2. Convert 50° Fahrenheit to Centigrade

$$(F° - 32°) \ 5/9 = C°$$
$$(50° - 32°) \ 5/9 =$$
$$18 \times 5/9 =$$
Then 50° F = 10° C

3. Convert 70° Fahrenheit to Absolute

$$(F - 32)5/9 = C; \ C + 273 = A$$
$$[(F - 32)5/9] + 273 =$$
$$[(70 - 32)5/9] + 273 =$$
$$(38 \times 5/9) + 273 =$$
$$21 + 273 = 294 \ 1/9° \ A$$
70° F = 294° A approximately

* For our purposes, rounding the answer off to the nearest whole number is sufficiently accurate.

It can be seen that Centigrade temperature can be converted to Absolute by adding 273. Since there are 180 Fahrenheit degrees for 100 Centigrade degrees the conversions are:

$$(1.8 \times \text{Centigrade}) + 32 = \text{Fahrenheit}$$
$$\text{and}$$
$$(\text{Fahrenheit} - 32) \times 5/9 = \text{Centigrade}$$

Note that 1.8 and 5/9 are reciprocal.

These scales are given for general information only. Where temperature is important in calculating volumes and pressures of gases, it is necessary to know how to convert from one scale to another. The gas laws use the Absolute, or Kelvin, temperature, and usual temperature changes can be ignored since 1° Kelvin at ordinary temperatures, say 70° F., would be the difference between about 294° and 295° or about 1 part in 300. An error of this amount is less than can be read on an ordinary pressure gauge. (The general rule on volume and pressure is discussed later in relation to filling cylinders.)

Contrary to common belief, temperature alone does not give a measure of heat, but merely an indication of relative "hotness" or "coldness" of an object. Certain practical knowledge is derived from a temperature measurement; for example, air temperatures may become uncomfortable above about 90° F. and below about 60° F. unless protective measures are taken. However man may tolerate air temperatures considerably higher and lower for considerable periods of time without any serious or permanent effects. Tolerable water temperatures are confined to a much narrower range. In general, water colder than 70° F. cannot be endured indefinitely by the unprotected swimmer, and from 60° F. downward good protective suits are required. Water above 80° F. becomes uncomfortable if much activity is carried on. The degree of comfort or discomfort experienced in water at any given temperature will vary among individuals, depending upon personal differences, state of nutrition, health, age, etc., but the general values given above will be valid for the average person. The difference in tolerable temperatures between a gaseous and liquid environment depends upon heat capacity rather than upon temperature.

Heat is energy and is usually measured in calories or in thermal units; for most of our discussion we will use the calorie, which is that amount of heat required to raise the temperature of 1 gram of water by 1 degree Centigrade (453 grams equal 1 pound). It therefore requires about 100 calories to raise the temperature of 1 gram of water from the freezing to the boiling point. Energy is required for melting and for vaporization as well as for raising temperature. Ice at a temperature of 0° C. requires about 80 calories per gram to convert it to water, and water at 100° C. requires about 540 calories per gram to convert it to steam. Ice at 0° C. and steam at 100° C. therefore differ in heat content by 80 + 100 + 540, or 720 calories per gram, while water at these temperatures differs by only 100 calories. While water varies in heat content by about 1 calorie per gram per degree, ice varies by about ½ calorie per degree. The amount of heat required to change the temperature of a material by one degree Centigrade is called the "specific heat" of that material.

TABLE I

SPECIFIC HEAT FOR SEVERAL COMMON SUBSTANCES

Material	Specific Heat Calories/Gram*
Air	0.25
Water	1.00
Iron	0.11
Copper	0.10
Aluminum	0.22
Lead	0.03

* Values from the *Handbook of Chemistry and Physics*, 29th ed. (Cleveland: Chemical Rubber Publishing Co.).

If we compare the cooling capacities of air and water it is evident from Table I that, pound for pound, water will absorb four times as much heat as that required by air for the same temperature change. On a volume basis, water is about 900 times as heavy as air at sea level; therefore, on a volume basis, water absorbs 900 × 4 or about 3,600 times as much heat as air to bring about a comparable temperature change. It should also be pointed out that water is better than air as a conductor of heat and will therefore remove heat from the body more rapidly. The high heat capacity and heat conductivity of water make it necessary to use some type of protection in almost any extended periods in the water except in the warmest climates. The following table gives some values for heat conductivity of some suit types:

TABLE II

SOME VALUES FOR HEAT CONDUCTIVITY OF SOME SUIT TYPES

Material	Conductivity*
Bare skin	65.00
⅛" natural rubber	9.60
¼" wool underwear (stillwater)	13.40
¼" underwear (dry) under ⅛" rubber suit	0.68

* Expressed in British Thermal Units per hour per square foot of material per degree Fahrenheit temperature difference across the material.

From Table II it is evident that almost any type of suit affords considerable protection; but the human body has 15 to 20 square feet of surface and a British Thermal Unit equals about 252 calories, so considerable quantities of heat can be lost in any cold water even with the best suits. The popular foam rubber or neoprene suits offer about the same degree of thermal protection as a thin, dry suit over wool underwear if certain other factors are considered. If ¼-inch foam material is "skinned" or coated on only one side, water enters the open bubbles on the inner surface and thus considerably reduces the effective thickness. Material of ⁵⁄₁₆ or ⅜ inch which is coated or "skinned" on both surfaces offers about the maximum protection that one can expect. (Thicker suits present a buoyancy problem, as we shall see later.) Thin, "dry" suits, while affording good protection, are sometimes difficult to seal properly, and tend to tear easily when in contact with rough or sharp objects. A break in the wet suit is not so serious but, in cold water, leaks in a dry suit markedly reduce its insulating efficiency, as can be seen in the difference between the values for wet and dry underwear. Also, if a leak develops in a dry suit worn over underwear, a considerable change in buoyancy can be experienced as the trapped air in the underwear is replaced by water. A well-fit dry suit may be worn over a wet suit for maximum protection and a minimum loss of both buoyancy and insulation in the event the dry suit is torn.

Precise values for the heat conductivity of wet suits cannot be given, since these depend upon the type of material, unicellular bubble size, and bubble integrity, and upon whether the material is finished on one or both sides. Any good quality material in a well-tailored suit should meet almost all sport or recreational diving requirements; for the best results, a suit must be well fitted.

A word of caution is necessary here in regard to the general application of the values in Table II. When diving without a protective suit, the average skin temperature can be considered equivalent to water temperature, so heat loss is a gradual process from the warmer deep tissues to the surface. Temperature difference between the body surface and the body core will vary with the type of suit and the degree of exercise as well as water temperature. Therefore, the only way to determine actual heat loss is by direct measurement known as calorimetry, which is a difficult technique.

Gas, Pressure, and the Gas Laws

One of the most interesting things about physics is the systematic way in which all natural phenomena are associated in a continuous manner and a direct relationship. While this statement cannot be fully developed here, its validity can be readily seen in a brief study of heat, pressure, and the gas laws.

All matter is composed of molecules. These molecules are constantly in motion. In solids this motion consists of vibrations of the molecule about its fixed "average" position. The fixed position is determined by the forces of other molecules that surround it. The frequency and amplitude of these vibrations are determined by the amount of thermal energy (heat and energy are synonymous) the molecules contain.

For example, in ice, the water molecules are held in a crystalline structure because the forces of attraction between water molecules are greater than the energy required for free movement. Ice is therefore solid. If the temperature is increased the energy of the molecules becomes so great that they can slide past each other (but still be held in close proximity), and the mass of ice starts to "flow" or become liquid. When sufficient heat is attained (at the boiling point) molecules gain enough energy to overcome the forces of attraction completely and escape to become a gas.

Air is a mixture of the gases (or vapors) of oxygen (about 21 per cent), nitrogen (78 per cent), and small amounts of carbon dioxide and less common substances. The composition of "air" is generally quite constant everywhere, and precise values are given in Table III. It should be recognized that these values may vary in certain special cases and that the exact composition is also dependent upon the amount of water vapor or "humidity." Air analysis is usually expressed in percentages of "dry" air unless otherwise stated.

TABLE III

PRECISE VALUES OF AIR COMPOSITION

Gas	Per Cent	Partial mm Hg	Pressure psi	Atmos- pheres	Feet of Salt Water
Nitrogen (N_2)	78.00	592.8	11.5	.780	25.74
Oxygen (O_2)	21.00	159.6	3.09	.21	6.93
Carbon Dioxide (CO_2)	.03	.23	.004	.0003	.01
Others	.97	7.37	.106	.0097	.32
TOTAL	100.00	760.00	14.700	1.0000	33.00

Also shown in Table III and in Figure 1 are examples of Dalton's Law, which states that "In a mixture of gases, each gas exerts a pressure proportional to the percentage of the total gas which it represents." In air there are approximately 21 molecules of oxygen in each 100 molecules of total gas. About 1/5 of the total number of molecular collisions therefore involve an oxygen molecule. Thus oxygen exerts about 1/5 of the total pressure. These fractions are called the partial pressures of the various gases. This is an important factor in diving, since the body functions are more directly influenced by the individual or partial pressures of metabolically active gases (such as oxygen or carbon dioxide) than by total pressure. In very deep diving, mixtures with as little as 4 per cent oxygen are used to keep the partial pressures of oxygen ($_pO_2$) below toxic levels.

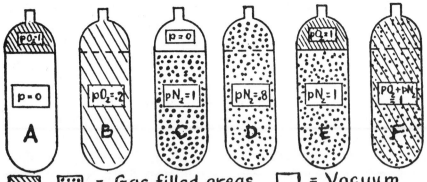

FIG. 1. DALTON'S LAW OF PARTIAL PRESSURES

P = Pressure. O_2 = Oxygen. N_2 = Nitrogen.
A. Oxygen at one atmosphere occupies ⅕ of volume.
B. Oxygen now occupies total volume; P = .2 atmosphere.
C. Nitrogen at one atmosphere occupies ⅘ of volume.
D. Nitrogen occupies total volume; P = .8 atmosphere.
E. Oxygen ⅕, Nitrogen ⅘, both at one atmosphere.
F. Oxygen and Nitrogen mixed; total P = 1 atmosphere.
E and F combine A, B, C, D to show gases exert pressure
directly proportional to percentage in a mixture.

As gas molecules move about they frequently collide with each other and with solid surfaces in their vicinity. If a solid wall had gas on only one side, the force of these collisions would tend to drive the wall in the direction of the impact. This force is measured as pressure. If the gas is "squeezed" so that the molecules occupy a smaller volume, the number of collisions increases and we thus have a "higher pressure." This is the situation with the gaseous atmosphere around the earth.

If we could obtain a column of air 1 square inch in cross-sectional area and extending from sea level up to the outermost air layer and weigh it, the weight would be approximately 14.7 pounds. This 14.7 pounds per square inch (psi) we call "one atmosphere of pressure absolute." A similar column of air taken from an altitude of 18,000 feet to the uppermost layers would weigh only 7.35 pounds or ½ an atmosphere. Since 18,000 feet is only a small fraction of the thickness of the air around the earth, it is obvious that about one half of the total gas is packed (or compressed) within this comparatively thin film. Pressures are usually measured with gauges that are balanced to read zero at sea level when they are open to the air. "Gauge pressure" is therefore converted to absolute pressure by adding 1 if the gauge is calibrated to read in atmospheres, or 14.7 if the dial reads in pounds per square inch, or by adding 33 feet of salt water.

In everyday usage one atmosphere of pressure can be considered to be 15 rather than 14.7 pounds per square inch. This simplification represents an error of only about 2 per cent, which is below the probable error of a single reading in an ordinary diving pressure gauge. Another simplifying step is to use depth of water instead of pressure in making calculations. This is possible, since water is not compressible and pressure increases uniformly with depth. Pressure thus increases at a rate of 0.445 pounds per square inch per foot of depth in sea water and 0.432 pounds per square inch per foot of depth in fresh water. One additional atmosphere of pressure is experienced for every 33 feet of sea water or 34 feet of fresh water.

It is now necessary to examine the behavior of gas under conditions of changing temperature and pressure. Two fundamental laws apply: Charles' Law and Boyle's Law. Charles' Law states that "if pressure is held constant, the volume of a gas will vary directly with the absolute temperature." The law can also be stated: "if the volume of a gas is held constant the pressure will vary directly with the absolute temperature." Expressed mathematically:

$$P \text{ (pressure)} = kT \text{ (absolute temperature)}$$
$$\text{and} \quad V \text{ (volume)} = kT \text{ (absolute temperature)}$$

where the k is a proportionality constant, which makes the statement an equation. The two expressions may be combined and stated as

$$PV = kT$$

The combined statement also represents Boyle's Law, which says that at a constant temperature, the volume of a gas varies inversely with pressure. These relationships may be easily checked with a toy balloon filled with air and dipped in water at varying temperature or taken from the surface to the bottom of the deep end of a pool (constant temperature).

Since the above equations are scientific laws, they must hold for all conditions. Therefore, if a given amount of gas under a specified set of conditions P_1, V_1, and T_1, is moved to a new environment, P_2, V_2, and T_2, the first equation may be divided by the second (since both sides of each equation are equal) and the constant cancels out.

$$\frac{P_1 V_1}{P_2 V_2} = \frac{k T_1}{k T_2}$$

For small changes in absolute temperature (such as those encountered in ordinary diving) the ratio of T_1 / T_2 will be nearly unity. Since the error introduced by assuming the ratio to be 1 for small temperature changes is again within the limit of error in reading the usual type of diving pressure gauge, the equation can be rewritten in this form:

$$\frac{P_1 V_1}{P_2 V_2} = 1 \text{ or } P_1 V_1 = P_2 V_2$$

With this relationship established we can now make some further simplifying assumptions—first, that V is the volume of free air to be delivered by the cylinder; second, that the P in the equation is the ambient pressure at depth; and third, the amount of air breathed per breath and the number of breaths per minute will not materially change with depth. With these assumptions we can begin to solve simple problems to determine the length of time any given air supply will last at any given depth.

In order to apply the following calculations a diver should first determine his rate of air usage in the water. Let us assume a diver will use 1 cubic foot of air per minute at the surface and has a tank holding 72 cubic feet of air when charged to 2,100 pounds. If the tank is full, it will deliver 72 cubic feet of air at the surface; how much will it deliver at a depth of 30 feet in fresh water, and how long will it last? (Remember that 34 feet is equal to 1 atmosphere pressure change, and there is 1 atmosphere at the surface.)

34 (depth equivalent at the surface) $\times$ 72 (cubic feet) will be equal to the pressure at depth times the volume delivered at depth $(34 + 30) \times V_2$

$$\text{or } 34 \times 72 = 64 \times V_2$$

$$\frac{(P_1)}{(P_2)} \frac{34}{64} \times 72 \, (V_1) = V_2$$

$$\text{or } .531 \times 72 = 38.2$$

The cylinder will deliver 38 cubic feet of air at 30 feet, or it will last 38 minutes.

An inspection of the gas laws will also indicate that the volume of gas in a cylinder will vary directly with the gauge pressure. In a cylinder rated for 72 cubic feet at 2,100 psia how much gas will the cylinder deliver if the gauge reads 1,400 psia?

$$\frac{1,400}{2,100} \times 72 \text{ cu. ft.} = \frac{2}{3} \times 72 = 48$$

How long would this tank last at 66 feet in sea water?

$$\frac{33}{33 + 66} \times 48 = \frac{1}{3} \times 48 = 16 \text{ cu. ft. or 16 minutes}$$

In making these depth-time calculations the diver should *always* remember that P_2 is the pressure to which he is going. For example, if a diver determines before entering the water that he can stay at 40 feet for 30 minutes, and after 15 minutes wishes to ascend to 20 feet, how long will his gas supply last? Note that he has 15 minutes left at 40 feet (sea water).

$$P_1 = 33 + 40$$
$$P_2 = 33 + 20$$

The equation is thus

$$\frac{73}{53} \times 15 = 1.38 \times 15 = 20^+ \text{ minutes}$$

The equation may be simplified as follows:

$$\frac{\text{volume of gas in cylinder}}{\left[\dfrac{\text{depth} + 33}{33}\right] \times \dfrac{\text{respiratory minute}}{\text{volume at surface}}} = \text{time at depth}$$

The above calculations assume that the cylinder will be *empty* at the end of the dive. Calculations should *always allow a margin of safety*, and a dive should always be planned to terminate with an ample reserve in the cylinder. Every diver should work with the gas law equation and with his own air requirements so that the above kind of calculations become almost automatic.

The same gas laws apply to skin diving as well as to scuba diving. If a diver fills his lungs with air at the surface and skin-dives to 34 feet in fresh water he will have half a lungful:

$$\frac{P_1}{P_2} V_1 = V_2 = \frac{34 \text{ (surface equivalent)}}{34 + 34 \text{ (depth equivalent)}} = \tfrac{1}{2} V_1$$

Most people cannot reduce the air volume in their lungs below one fifth of the filled volume. A large percentage cannot get below one fourth of the volume without practice. The compression of gas in the respiratory system "dead spaces" such as sinuses, face plate, wind pipe, etc., further limits the depth to which a breath-hold dive may be made. Exceeding safe limits can result in "squeeze" (discussed in Chapter 3, "Medical Aspects of Diving: Underwater Physiology").

This also works in reverse for a scuba diver attempting to ascend from depth while holding his breath. If the diver has his lungs full at 66 feet (sea water) and ascends without exhaling, the gas will attempt to expand according to the equation

$$\frac{P_1}{P_2} \frac{(33 + 66)}{33} \times 1 \text{ lungful} = 3 \text{ lungfuls}$$

Since the lungs cannot expand to accommodate this volume, the pressure will increase to the point of rupturing the lungs. (The consequences of such an event are also discussed in detail in Chapter 3.) Just remember to keep breathing or to exhale on the way up when diving with scuba gear.

Before leaving the gas laws Henry's Law should also be mentioned. This states that "the amount of any given gas that will dissolve in a liquid at a given temperature is a function of the partial pressure of that gas in contact with the liquid." Since a large percentage of the human body is water the law simply states that as one dives deeper and deeper, more gas will dissolve in the body tissues and that upon ascent, the dissolved gas must be given off. (The significance of this phenomenon coupled with the comparatively slow rates of solution in and release of gas from body tissues are developed fully in the discussion of decompression in Chapter 3.)

Density and Buoyancy

If one lifts a 2-ounce fishline sinker he refers to it as "heavy," but a large block of balsa wood or similar material is called "light," even though it may weigh twice as much. The term *density* reconciles this discrepancy, since it is an expression of mass (or weight) per unit volume. A small "heavy" object is one that has a high density and is "heavy" by virtue of comparison with some less dense material. Relative density is also expressed in terms of specific gravity.

The densities of various materials are compared by means of their specific gravities. The specific gravity of water is arbitrarily set at 1.0. If the weight per unit volume (density) of another material is twice that of water, it thus has a specific gravity of 2.0. If the specific gravity of a substance is 0.5, its density is half that of water.

Archimedes' principle states that a body immersed in a liquid is buoyed upward by a force equal to the weight of the water it displaces. This says, in effect, that a body which is relatively less dense than water (specific gravity less than 1) will float, while one which has a density greater than that of water will sink. When such a body is totally submerged it will have an effective weight less than its weight in air by an amount equal to the weight of water displaced. Thus, a block of wood with a specific gravity of 0.8 will float with 0.2 of its volume exposed above the surface, while a body with a specific gravity of 2.0 will sink but will weigh only one half of its weight in air while submerged.

The density of the human body is very nearly equal to that of water, and a diver may normally ascend or descend at will. Small changes in buoyancy usually are not a serious problem; large changes may be quite significant. Small changes are encountered in scuba diving as a result of emptying the air cylinders. A charge of air may weigh between 3 and 10 pounds depending on the size and type of air cylinder used. Most open-circuit breathing devices are near neutral in sea water when the tanks are empty, but they readily sink when tanks are filled.

Since the fluid and solid tissues of the body are incompressible and the volume of the gas spaces are maintained by the use of scuba, no buoyancy change results from the increased pressure on the body. Excessive air trapped in a rubber suit can be hazardous if carried to depths or if lost even in comparatively shallow water.

Archimedes' principle is the basis of various safety devices that float a distressed diver to the surface. Most of these are inflated by a mechanical device to puncture the seal on a small CO_2 cylinder. These puncture devices and the CO_2 cylinders should be inspected frequently to ensure smooth operation and to be certain that the cylinder has not corroded through or been damaged so that the charge is lost. It should also be noted that CO_2 is a gas which does not obey the ideal gas laws in that it is much more compressible than most other common gases found in air. Therefore it will not extend the float bladder as much at depth as would be calculated from a measurement made on the surface.

Density (and viscosity) also control the maximum rates of movement of bodies through water. The drag resistance is a function of the profile presented to the water and varies in direct proportion to the square of the velocity.

For example, a buoyancy of 3 pounds would give a man in upright position with legs together a maximum velocity of about 100 feet per minute; if the legs are spread 2 feet apart this may be reduced to 50 or 60 feet per minute. Since resistance is a function of the square of the velocity, increasing the buoyancy to 12 pounds would only double the maximum rate of rise.

This is important in swimming, also, since doubling the speed would place a fourfold workload on the swimmer. Since about 0.8 or 0.9 miles per hour is a good average swim rate with scuba it becomes quite obvious that doubling the rate would be next to impossible. For this reason, it is absolutely essential to know how currents are running and your own capacity.

Humidity

Vapor tension, or the pressure exerted by "escaped" or gaseous particles of a substance, is determined by the temperature and is, for our purposes, independent of the total pressure. Therefore, a cylinder of 1 cubic foot capacity has no more water vapor when it is charged to 2,100 pounds than when it is "empty." This is true even with liquid air in the cylinder. It may be assumed, then, that breathing air delivered by a regulator will always be "dry." Continued breathing of this dry air may produce an uncomfortable dryness in the mouth and throat. Such dryness is alleviated by removing the mouthpiece (or admitting water in the mask, as with full-face masks) and taking a drink or at least rinsing out the mouth.

Exhaled air is saturated with water vapor at body temperature. This exhaled moisture condenses in the breathing tubes and/or mask. If the water is cold, enough moisture may collect in the breathing tubes after a time to suggest a leak. The water is easily blown out through the exhaust valve and presents no problem, except in very cold weather, freezing may occur.

Moisture from the breath used to equalize pressure in the face plate may also condense on the glass and result in fogging. Evaporation from the skin and eyes will also contribute to this problem. Moistening the glass with saliva or applying a commercial "anti-fog" compound will usually prevent any difficulty of this nature. In some cases it is advantageous to keep a small amount of water in the face plate to rinse the glass occasionally.

Illumination and Vision

Vision under the surface of the water is modified by two of the physical properties, which are markedly different between air and water: refractive index and light penetration.

The index of refraction of a substance is the ratio of the speed of light in a vacuum to its speed in the substance. Light travels in water at about three fourths of its speed in air. This difference in velocity causes light rays to be "bent," when they pass from air into water or from water into air.

Because of the difference in "refractive index" between air and water, there is some visual displacement of images even under ideal conditions. Under conditions where the eye is in direct contact with the water, it loses its normal lens characteristics. Since it is unable to correct for this difference, considerable distortion results. When an air layer is interposed by using a face mask, this difficulty is eliminated. However, the difference in refractive index now comes into play. The distortion ratio is 3 to 4. Objects appear to be closer than the actual distance and correspondingly larger; angles are distorted. This poses problems in spearing fish and in photography. For these activities it is best to calibrate photographic equipment individually and to learn to accommodate to this phenomenon.

Particles in water that are extremely small also diffract light and cause a "fuzzy" image. "Fuzzy," or blurred, pictures may be taken quite easily by simply neglecting to include a packet of silica gel or other moisture-control compound in the camera case. If the camera case is closed in moist air (as it usually is aboard a boat or on the beach) this moisture may condense on the face of the case or the camera lens when taken into cold water.

Peter Stackpole found, during the filming of Walt Disney's *Twenty Thousand Leagues Under the Sea*, that using a wide-angle lens and setting the range at about 70 per cent of the actual distance corrected most of this distortion. Exposure varied with depth and was determined with the aid of an exposure meter in the watertight camera case. (See *U.S. Camera*, 17 [1954], 51.)

The problem of vision is further complicated by the limited penetration of light into the water. Where visibility is usually good (little or no turbidity or plankton) and the water is deep, photography becomes difficult beyond 100 feet in depth without artificial light. When the sun is not directly overhead or when the surface is riffled, light is further reduced.

Color photography is a more serious problem, since the colors are differentially absorbed. Warm colors are absorbed first with reds being removed in the first few feet, followed by orange at about 15, and yellow at around 30 feet. Beyond 60 feet blues predominate and gradually deepen into darkness. The best underwater color photographs can be taken with artificial light either at night or at depths where sunlight is a negligible factor.

Only a very few points on photography can be mentioned here. The camera fan should consult some of the many excellent books and magazine articles which have been written on underwater photographic equipment and techniques.

Acoustics

In 1953 Captain J. Y. Cousteau published his well-known *The Silent World*, depicting the pleasures of self-contained diving (and a few of its hazards). Despite the impression left by this book, the submarine environment is not a "silent world." In some areas it is, in fact, extremely noisy. According to some reports, great pains must be taken to find and maintain waters sufficiently "silent" for the testing and calibrating of sonar and other underwater sound equipment.

The sounds heard beneath the surface arise from waves, surf, rocks, and gravel moving with the water, boats, and even the marine life, such as fish, shrimps, and crabs.

Sound travels more rapidly in water (about 4,800 feet per second) than in air (about 1,090 feet per second), and certain noises can be heard for greater distances. In spite of this, it is difficult to use the voice for satisfactory communications under water. The difference in such factors as inertia and viscosity between air and water is such that only about 1 part in 10,000 of the sound energy actually enters the water when speaking into an ordinary mask. In compressed air scuba this is further complicated by the noise produced from escaping air during exhalation and speaking.

Speaking diaphragms of metal or plastic may help considerably when properly located in a mask but, at best, permit conversation only over comparatively short distances. Even under optimum conditions it is difficult to attract the attention of a buddy some distance away by voice alone.

Banging on the air tanks with the butt of a knife handle or stone produces a sharp, loud noise which can be readily picked up for quite a distance. This is a very satisfactory way of passing information when a standard set of signals has been worked out. Hitting stones together or cavitating the water by sharp claps of the hands also produce clear signals.

The higher velocity of sound in water and some differences in the mode of hearing under water make localization of sound more difficult than in air. Many divers find it very hard to locate a sound source by hearing alone.

Though this chapter is by no means a complete picture of all the problems encountered in diving, it should provide sufficient background to permit a better understanding of the factors which tend to make every dive either pleasant or disagreeable, a success or a failure.

3

MEDICAL ASPECTS OF DIVING: UNDERWATER PHYSIOLOGY

By Edward H. Lanphier, M.D.

Medical science is concerned with just about anything which can happen to the human body. What happens to it in diving is no exception. The way the surroundings and the activity itself affect the body, and how the body reacts to them, set the limits to what a diver can do and involve most of the things which can harm him. These are clearly medical matters, but they cannot just be left to the doctors. In fact, a diver who hopes to be effective and safe in the water has to know a lot more about these particular medical matters than the average dry-land doctor does. They add up to a somewhat grim subject, but diving is one place where ignorance and bliss are two different things.

The preceding chapter, "Physics as Related to Diving," told about the main elemental forces which confront the diver under water. The medical part—how those forces act on the body and how the body reacts—can be called physiology. Physiology is one of the basic sciences of medicine, dealing with the way the body operates under different conditions, normal and abnormal. This chapter will consider particularly underwater physiology. Equally medical and equally important matters like physical qualifications, first aid, marine-life injuries, and the problem of cold are taken up in other chapters.

Since the word "diving" is applied to just about any method of getting underwater, from springboards to submarines, we shall have to narrow the definition down a bit. As far as this chapter is concerned, a diver is (1) underwater, bare or in a flexible suit, and thus exposed to *increased surrounding pressure;* he is (2) staying down longer than he can hold his breath, and thus must somehow be supplied with *something to breathe.*

If he meets these criteria, he's a diver regardless of what he is doing down there or what he calls himself. This highhanded approach not only defines the term but also indicates the two big "Facts of Life" which are involved. Almost all the physiological difficulties stem from one or both of these, and they can arise whether one dives with air hose or with scuba.

Direct Effects of Pressure

You will recall that pressure increases rather rapidly as you descend in the water. As a rough rule of thumb, it increases about 1 pound per square inch (psi) with each 2 feet of descent. (A more exact figure is 0.445 psi per foot of depth.)

Another way of looking at the pressure changes of descent is to consider that we are already under pressure at the surface—14.7 psi, 760 millimeters of mercury, 29.9 inches of mercury, or *1 atmosphere*. Each 33 feet of descent will add another "atmosphere" to the total, or absolute, pressure. The pressure at 33 feet of depth is two atmospheres, absolute, and so on. The "atmosphere" system is the easiest to use in considering many aspects of pressure. These relationships are worth remembering:

TABLE IV

INCREASE OF PRESSURE WITH INCREASE OF DEPTH

Pressure (atmospheres, absolute)	Depth (feet)
1	surface
2	33
3	66
4	99
5	132
6	165
10	297
	and so on down . . .

The term "absolute" indicates that the pressure already existing at the surface has been taken into account—as it must be in order to consider pressure-volume relationships, partial pressures, and the like. Since talking in atmospheres usually implies absolute pressures, it is not always specified as such. (Incidentally, all the figures given here are for sea water, assuming a specific gravity of 1.025—that sea water is 1.025 times as heavy as fresh water. In fresh water it takes 34 feet of descent instead of 33 to add an atmosphere of pressure, for example.)

How Does Pressure Act?

The effects of pressure can be classified into two categories: "direct" (or "primary") and "indirect" (or "secondary").

The direct effects are largely mechanical and fairly obvious. The indirect ones are more subtle, and understanding them requires digging a little deeper into physiology. They come about mainly through the partial pressures of the gases which the diver breathes. For this reason, they will be easier to handle after we've talked about that second big factor in diving: "something to breathe."

The direct effects of pressure are produced either (1) by way of a pressure difference built up across some structure of the body, or (2) by way of a change in gas volume. In most cases, these two are actually very closely related, but the first is the more basic idea.

Unless a pressure difference or "differential" exists, pressure does not have any significant direct, mechanical effects. Living tissue as such can be exposed to pressures equivalent to several thousands of feet of depth without showing any structural change. Being largely fluid, living tissue is no more compressible than the water and simply transmits the pressure throughout itself without building up any differentials or showing any volume change.

The same is true of the body parts which are "solid tissues." For example, taking one of your legs from one depth to another produces no more change than it would in a leg-shaped bag of water. But the body is not *all* a mass of solids and solutions like a leg. It contains certain *air spaces*, and others may be hitched onto its surface in the form of goggles, mask, and whatnot. The following are all potential trouble spots:

1. Spaces associated with the ears
2. The sinuses
3. The lungs and airways
4. Air pockets in the stomach and intestines
5. Any air space applied to the surface of the body

The body will transmit pressure freely through all its "fluid" portions directly to, but not necessarily into, these air spaces. If the space has a soft, movable wall, this pressure will simply cause the space to collapse until the air inside is compressed to the appropriate volume for that pressure (remember Boyle's Law). Once this volume is reached, nothing more will happen.

If the space has a semirigid wall and will not compress freely, the end result will be compromise—some compression of the gas, and some pressure difference across the wall. If the space is walled by bone, for example, the pressure inside will remain what it was to start with while the outside pressure goes up. Here, the whole surrounding pressure (above one atmosphere) can act as a differential. But if a rigid or semirigid space is connected to a source of air at ambient (surrounding) pressure, the developing differential will simply force air into the space until the difference in pressure is *equalized*. The amount of air required to equalize also follows the Boyle's Law relationship: if a rigid space is equalized at 33 feet, it will contain twice as many air molecules as it did at the surface, and so forth.

When the ambient pressure is reduced, these processes simply go into reverse. A "soft" space will just re-expand, and nothing will happen unless the expanding gas overfills it. An equalized rigid space will simply vent the extra gas if the connection remains open. If there is overfilling or blockage, of course a differential will develop—higher pressure inside the space than outside.

All injuries resulting from pressure differences can be lumped under the term "barotrauma" (injury due to pressure), but the "up" and "down" troubles are best discussed separately.

Pressure Effects in Descent—"Squeeze"

For a long time, divers' jargon has included the word "squeeze." It is so descriptive that it has come to be applied to virtually all the troubles that pressure can cause during *descent*, or as a result of pressure differentials between two structures or spaces.

Fig. 2.   Squeeze

Actually, the accident which gave rise to the word was what happened to a suit-and-helmet diver when his air hose broke near the surface and vented the helmet to lower pressure or when he *fell* to a greater depth or otherwise descended "ahead" of his air supply. Either mishap caused the pressure in the helmet to be lower than the pressure outside. Then, the helmet formed a rigid space with one "soft" wall—namely the diver himself. You can fill in the rest of the picture yourself. The tales about divers being buried in their helmets are not just sea stories. Similar but less drastic accidents have also happened with hose-supplied face-mask diving rigs. This kind of squeeze is rather rare now that air hoses are usually equipped with non-return valves; but the danger involved in falling remains, and it can show up even in scuba.

Although scuba divers do not have to worry about this exact form of squeeze very often, there are still plenty of situations in which the same mechanisms of local differences in pressure can operate.

Middle Ear Squeeze

What can happen to the middle ear serves as a good example. Figure 3 will help illustrate this.

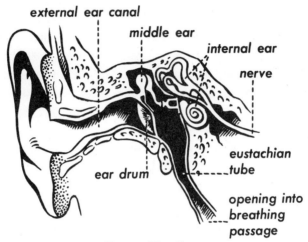

FIG. 3. THE EAR

Consider the space marked "middle ear." When you leave the surface, this contains air at surface pressure. As you descend, the ambient pressure increases, but the internal pressure does not. This clearly produces a differential across the drum. In addition, the body is transmitting the pressure to the walls of the space as well: the blood pressure is going up along with the ambient pressure, and this means that the same differential is operating across the walls of every blood vessel in the membrane lining.

Normally, before any of the differentials get very high, you can get air at ambient pressure from the throat to go through the Eustachian tube and equalize the pressure. But the tube doesn't always pass air very readily. You may have to do some yawning, swallowing, jaw moving, or other maneuvers to get the tube to open. A few people have voluntary control over certain muscles and can open it at will, but most aren't so lucky. It may even be necessary to grab your nose and blow to get air started through; but if you blow too hard, the "trap door" may just shut tighter.

A few people never can "pop their ears" because of some structural difficulty. Anyone will have trouble if a cold, infection, or hay fever causes the membranes around the opening to swell. In these cases, using nose drops, spray, or an inhaler may shrink the membranes enough to make equalization possible. But it never pays to push yourself when you have trouble.

If equalization gets too far behind as you descend, the trap door effect may make it impossible to catch up without first coming up a few feet.

If it is impossible to equalize by getting air in through the tube, and you keep going, what happens then? Those blood vessels are usually the first thing to get into trouble; and since the membrane lining continues over the inner surface of the drum, blood vessel troubles appear in the drum also. In fact, the results can be seen by the doctor looking at the drum through his otoscope.

The vessels are not designed to take much pressure, and the differential will squeeze a lot of blood into them. So they go through a definite series of stages. Just how far they go depends on how bad the squeeze is and how long it lasts. (1) The vessels dilate—become much larger than usual. (2) They start leaking—the fluid part of the blood oozes out and causes swelling of the membrane. (3) They burst—causing actual bleeding into the tissue.

If the swelling and bleeding process goes very far, the membrane is "blown up" and starts to peel off the bony wall. Before this has gone very far, the surface of the lining will break and let blood flow directly into the middle ear space.

The drum itself will become a bloody mess during this process, and eventually it will break (rupture) if the squeeze is bad enough. Sometimes, however, there will be enough hemorrhage into the space to reduce the air volume and equalize pressure in that way before the drum gives way.

This "squeeze" process sounds painful, and it generally is. That is good because pain usually gives warning before much damage is done. A few people have drums or membranes so delicate that they can have damage without much pain, and this is quite a disadvantage.

It takes only a few feet of descent without equalization to cause discomfort and the beginning of trouble. Even as little as ten feet of such descent may cause serious damage, including rupture of the drum. Damage is not something you can take lightly, even though it *usually* heals up without much trouble. For one thing, free blood in the space makes a nice culture medium for germs, and the damaged membrane is in no shape to fight off infection. Infection can delay healing and form scar tissue, and deafness can result.

Without infection even a ruptured drum will usually heal up in a couple of weeks. Lesser damage may require only a few days. Normally, the only treatment is "hands off"—which means keeping *everything* which might carry infection (including medicine, fingers and all implements, and especially water) strictly *out* of the ear. It is always advisable to see a doctor and let him keep track of anything but a very slight ear injury. If there is an increase of pain after the injury, or if drainage appears, you should see a doctor at once. You may have some blood in your nasal secretions (or spit up traces) for a few hours after injury because blood from the middle ear will drain down the tube. In case of rupture, you *must not* dive again until the doctor says the drum has healed and until you are sure you can equalize without trouble.

Rupturing the ear drum in cold water can have very impressive effects. Cold water getting into the middle ear will cause a violent upset in the sense of balance resulting in marked dizziness and nausea. Although this will usually pass off as soon as the water warms up—a minute or so—things can be pretty tense in the meantime. You just have to "hang on." Don't try to surface unless your dive-buddy can take charge. You literally won't know which way is up until the effect subsides.

The *external ear canal* is also subject to squeeze if it gets closed up for any reason. (This possibility will be discussed under "external air spaces.")

Sinus Squeeze

There are four pairs of paranasal sinuses: (1) maxillaries—in the cheek bones, below the eyes; (2) frontals—in the forehead, above the bridge of the nose; (3) ethmoid—between the eyes; (4) sphenoid —back under the brain.

These sinuses are cavities in the bones of the face and head. They are lined with a membrane which is continuous with that of the nose, run-

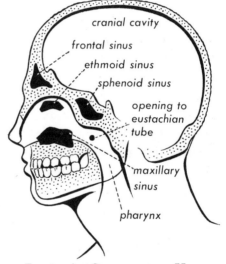

FIG. 4. AIR SINUSES IN THE HEAD

ning through the bony canals which connect the sinuses to the nose. If this membrane swells up where it goes through, it may shut off the sinus completely. This is not unusual during a bad cold, and it makes it impossible for the sinus to equalize.

Allowing for the obvious differences, almost everything said about the middle ear during squeeze will also apply to the sinuses, so you can fill in the details for yourself. Trying to take pressure when your sinuses won't equalize readily is asking for a good case of sinusitis. Sometimes nose drops and the like will help. There is, unfortunately, the possibility that the effect will have worn off by the time you need it most. Sometimes, a "rebound" effect—even more congestion than before—occurs. Vasoconstrictor products for oral use (tablets or capsules) are effective in some people, but many of these are combined with antihistamine drugs that can cause drowsiness.

Thoracic (Lung) Squeeze

The lungs and airways won't give trouble during descent as long as you keep breathing and are able to get plenty of air from your scuba. But if your air shuts off, or if you are just breath-hold diving to start with, difficulties can develop. Trying to breathe through a tube to the surface, if it is more than a foot long, will get you into the same kind of trouble.

Lacking additional air to equalize pressure, the lungs will simply be compressed, but only down to a certain point. They always contain a quart or so of air which can't be blown out no matter how hard you try and which can't be compressed any further without breaking something. This irreducible amount of air in the lungs is called the *residual volume*. Add to

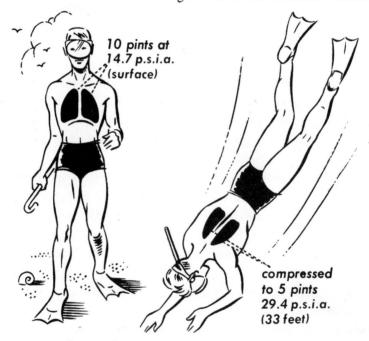

10 pints at 14.7 p.s.i.a. (surface)

compressed to 5 pints 29.4 p.s.i.a. (33 feet)

FIG. 5. PRESSURE EFFECTS ON LUNG VOLUME

this the volume of the airways themselves and the volume of any mask or breathing circuit you are using, and you have the barest minimum of air which the respiratory system can contain. If you have gone deep enough to compress the total volume you started with into this minimum volume, this is as far as you can go without squeeze unless you have an additional source of air.

The lungs consist of a mass of membrane even more delicate than that which lines the middle ear and sinuses. The blood vessels in this membrane will "give" long before the chest-cage itself takes much of a strain. The resulting bleeding and damage can be rough.

Navy Submarine Escape Training Tank instructors occasionally run into thoracic squeeze. Normally, most of them can "drop" the full 100-foot depth just holding their breath. But once in a while one will leave the surface with less air in his lungs than usual, or will lose air on the way down, and will unexpectedly reach his limit. If he keeps on going, the chances are he will surface coughing, wheezing, and bringing up bloody froth. Some never can make the full drop because their residual volume is large or their total lung volume is small by comparison.

"Gut" Squeeze

In a word, this doesn't happen. The structures in the gastrointestinal tract all have soft walls, so the air pockets simply compress with no differentials and no strain. The only possible trouble comes on ascent.

Squeeze in External Air Spaces

Mask or goggle squeeze. You have probably noticed that your face mask can pull quite a suction on your face as you descend and that you have to let air into it through your nose to keep the sensation from becoming severe. The mask is just trying to give you a *face squeeze.* Of course, a very flexible mask could take care of some of the pressure-difference just by flattening out on your face.

The most easily damaged tissues within a mask are the membranes which cover the surface of the eyeball and which line the lids and spaces around the eyeball. Hemorrhage can also occur behind the eyeball, in the socket. None of these possibilities is very pleasant. You can see why goggles, normally having no method of equalization, are bad business for anything but very shallow diving.

Suit squeeze. Any dry-type rubber suit will contain air spaces. Since the suit material has some body to it, these spaces can't flatten out 100 per cent completely—a little space between the material and the skin will remain, plus the air spaces of whatever you are wearing under the rubber. So when you descend in such a suit, your skin will tend to be squeezed wherever there is a space; and any body movement which requires separating the folds will increase the differential across the skin. Wherever one of these spaces can seal against the skin, the skin will be pulled into the space in the process. This may cause an uncomfortable pinching sensation. After the dive you may find lumps and ridges in the skin at such points, and there may even be some bleeding into the skin.

The cure for suit squeeze is to introduce just enough air into the suit to permit the spaces to return to their normal volume—to equalize. A few

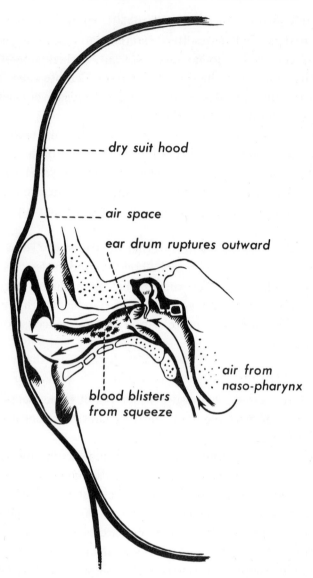

FIG. 6. Suit-Squeeze Effects of Dry Suit Hood on Ear

suits, like Cousteau's "constant volume" model, are equipped to make this equalization process easy. In a suit with the usual face-seal, you can generally blow air into the suit via the place where the face mask laps over the seal. There is one problem in this method of handling suit squeeze: if you are in the inverted position, any excess air will go to the feet. If there is much of it, you might find yourself held upside down and heading for the surface. (The Cousteau suit has a relief valve at each ankle to take care of this hazard.) "Wet suits" are normally free of such problems.

 External ear squeeze. As mentioned above, closing off the external ear canal can cause trouble very much like middle-ear squeeze. Ear plugs are bad business for this reason. Suits made of smooth rubber can occasionally seal over the external ear; but more often, external ear squeeze is just a part of a general suit squeeze as described above. Not only is there a bigger irreducible air space at that point, but the ear is a lot more delicate than the skin; so a suit squeeze can show up there even if it doesn't appear very noticeable elsewhere. The cure and cautions are the same.

This form of ear squeeze can damage either the canal lining or the drum or both. The usual result looks like a bunch of blood blisters; and if one of the blisters has burst, there will be bleeding from the external ear. In this case bleeding to the outside does *not* necessarily mean that the drum is ruptured, as it does in the middle-ear squeeze. However, the drum can rupture under this circumstance.

Miscellaneous. Squeeze due to external air spaces may show up occasionally in unusual forms. For instance, the concave undersides of snap fasteners on one type of scuba harness proved capable of producing extra nipples on manly chests. And then there was the case of transient marital incapacitation which resulted from a misadventure with a "Convenience" provided on one type of rubber suit.

GAS DENSITY EFFECTS

Another direct effect of pressure which ought to be mentioned happens to have nothing to do with the "squeeze" mechanism. It concerns the way air behaves once it is compressed.

If you notice that breathing is more difficult at depth, this is not just your imagination at work. The number of molecules packed into a volume of gas is directly proportional to the absolute pressure, but the volume you breathe remains about the same. The air you breathe at 100 feet is about four times as dense (as heavy) as air at the surface. If you are using open-circuit gear, each breath thus involves dragging four times as many molecules through your demand valve. Unless the scuba is very well designed, the extra effort required will be quite noticeable. In a homemade job you may just not get the air you need. Even moving the air through your own "pipes" is about twice as much work as it was at the surface. If you are free from asthma and other pulmonary conditions this doesn't involve much effort to start with; but trying to work very hard at depth may stop you.

DIRECT EFFECTS OF PRESSURE ON ASCENT

Most of the air spaces mentioned rarely give trouble when you come up. Even an ear or a sinus which gave you a bad time going down will usually behave. Air in suits, face masks, and the like just expands and escapes. (Of course, if you have an excess of air in your suit and no way for it to get out, it may give you unwanted buoyancy.)

Once in a great while, air pockets in the gut will give a bit of trouble. This might happen if a man swallowed air while he was on the bottom or if he had eaten some exceptionally potent baked beans or something similar. If the resulting gas were too far from either end to escape readily, it might overfill the gut and cause pain. It would probably work its way out one way or another without harm, but ascent should certainly be slowed down if abdominal pain develops.

Air embolism and lung damage. Unfortunately, the troubles which can result from gas expansion in the lungs are serious enough to make up for the rosy situation elsewhere—and then some.

Recalling Boyle's Law again: if a man is at 99 feet and ascends, the air in his lungs will undergo a fourfold expansion by the time he surfaces. The volume will double between 99 feet and 33 feet, and it will double again between 33 feet and surface. The actual rate of expansion becomes more and more rapid as he approaches the surface.

If the diver has much air in his lungs when he starts ascent, this expansion can fill the lungs completely, and any excess must be exhaled—or else.

The "or else" is quite sad. Failure to exhale promptly and adequately will cause the pressure in the lungs to rise above that in the rest of the body and on the outside. Once the lungs are fully expanded, the resulting differential will increase directly with the distance of further ascent. Since the lungs are very delicate, it does not take much of a differential like this to cause serious damage. The crucial amount of pressure is equivalent to about four feet of water. In other words, once the lungs have reached maximal expansion, *coming up only four feet more* can put you in real danger.

This is something to think about. For one thing, taking a really full breath on the bottom puts your lungs close to maximum expansion when you start. If you are practicing "ditching" a scuba and let the demand valve get much below your mouth while you are still breathing on it, you may be in some danger almost before you start. It is not surprising that cases of air embolism have been reported in ascents of ten feet or less, as in one case from the bottom of a swimming pool.

Consider what would happen if you are coming up rather fast and something causes you to hold your breath momentarily. Especially if you are close to the surface, your lungs could fill up very rapidly; and that deadly additional four feet of ascent wouldn't take long.

What, exactly, can happen? The most obvious thing is simply to *burst a lung*—an accident which is about as ugly as it sounds but which isn't necessarily fatal in itself. The most serious possibility is *air embolism*. With or without an obvious "burst," a pressure of around four feet of water can force air from the air sacs into the blood vessels which surround them. Once the air is in the vessels, it is carried rapidly to the heart. From there, it is pumped

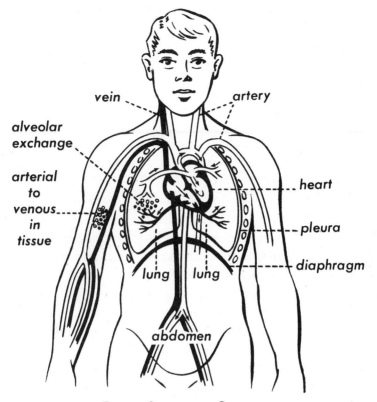

FIG. 7. CIRCULATORY SYSTEM

out into the arteries which supply the whole body. And these arteries are so arranged that some of the air is almost bound to go up the arteries which supply the brain.

Arteries look like the branches of a tree splitting and resplitting into finer and finer branches and twigs. Therefore, a bubble of any size much larger than a red corpuscle is bound to get stuck eventually. It will then form a plug (embolus) which will keep blood from flowing any farther in that particular branch. The brain tissue beyond the plug will be deprived of its blood supply; and it can survive such deprivation for only a few minutes without permanent damage.

A person who has suffered this kind of accident may be unconscious even before he reaches the surface; or he may climb out and appear normal for as long as a minute or two. It is possible to have a very small embolism with only limited symptoms, but this is rare. Usually, the victim collapses, loses consciousness, and may go into convulsions. Other signs, like showing bloody froth at the mouth, respiratory difficulty, and turning blue, will depend mainly on the extent of lung damage and the presence or absence or other consequences of overpressurization of the lungs. Sometimes the respiratory center will be involved in the embolism, and breathing will cease.

The only treatment with real hope of success is *prompt recompression*, and even this carries no guarantee. The principle here is to squeeze the bubble-plugs down to harmless size and get them to be absorbed. The necessity for prompt recompression is small comfort to scuba divers. They are rarely close enough to a chamber to do much good except in a mild case.

Recompression in the water with scuba is a rather forlorn hope. Successful treatment will usually require going to 165 feet; getting back up may take as long as thirty-eight hours. Just getting an unconscious man down to the "depth of relief" with a scuba, for example, would be hard enough, to say nothing of completing treatment that way. If a recompression chamber can be reached in any reasonable time, it would almost always be better to head for it at once than to spend time trying to treat the victim in the water. In the meantime, keeping him in a semi-inverted position to keep any more air from going to the brain, and giving him oxygen if possible, are about the only measures to suggest. If he is not breathing, artificial respiration should of course be given. One reported case and some animal experiments suggest that lowering the head (or rocking between horizontal and head-down position) may sometimes relieve an air embolism.

The other possible consequences of lung damage are usually far less serious, but they deserve mention:

Mediastinal emphysema—air forced into the tissue-spaces in the middle of the chest. Symptoms may include chest pain, trouble in breathing, trouble in swallowing, shock.

Treatment: Recompression if of serious degree. Otherwise, rest and general medical care.

Subcutaneous emphysema—air under the skin, usually around the base of the neck. This is not serious in itself, but it is often associated with mediastinal emphysema. Air in the neck region may interfere with talking, breathing, or swallowing.

Pneumothorax—air in the space between the lungs and the lining of the chest wall on either side. This will cause the affected lung to collapse at least partially and may interfere with breathing. If pressure builds up in the pneumothorax, the lung will be completely collapsed and the contents of the chest will be pushed over to the other side. Both breathing and heart action may be affected in this case.

Treatment: Recompression will give temporary relief, but often the pneumothorax will have to be relieved by insertion of a needle in the chest before the man can be brought up. This is definitely a job for the doctor.

PREVENTION is the key word in lung accidents. As a cause of death in scuba diving, these probably run drowning a very close second. Many of the cases are probably not recognized as such even on the autopsy table.

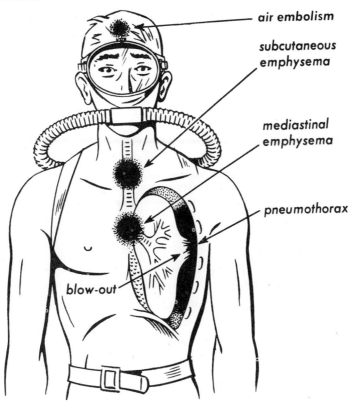

FIG. 8. POSSIBLE CONSEQUENCES OF OVERINFLATION OF THE LUNGS

In normal ascent with scuba, all you need to do is *breathe normally* throughout ascent. This keeps your "pipes" open.

Most of the accidents occur during emergency ascents where the scuba is either out of commission or has had to be left behind. Here, the big rule is *exhale continuously* and exhale even more if any sensation of pressure in the chest is noticed. If you are wearing fins, don't worry about exhaling to the point of losing buoyancy; you can always keep yourself coming up. Don't rush; come up about as fast as your bubbles.

Most emergency ascents are likely to occur in panic-type circumstances, and it is very contrary to instinct to exhale when you've lost your air supply under water. This is where a cool head and good training really pay off. Specific training in "free ascent" is very valuable, but the procedure should not be practiced from any depth unless a chamber is at hand and someone is in the water watching you.

The mechanics of starting ascent in an emergency are worth talking about. If you are wearing any kind of weights, they should be fastened in such a way that you can get rid of them almost instantaneously. Whether you should also ditch your scuba is debatable. Unless it is fouled or could otherwise hold you down, it seems better to leave it on even though it is useless. You will be in a much better position to get it off when you reach the surface. Even if it tends to hold you under, you can tread water enough to keep your head out and breathe while you are getting it off.

Wherever you dive, you should know the location of the nearest manned-and-ready recompression chamber and have plans for reaching it as rapidly as possible. The value of portable one-man chambers is debatable except where a large chamber is very distant.

Something to Breathe

"Why breathe?" That sounds like a silly question, but we don't often stop to think about it. Actually, the answer is quite a story. But in a word, we breathe because the body *consumes oxygen* and *produces carbon dioxide* in the process of living and working. Oxygen has to be taken in from what we breathe, and carbon dioxide has to be dumped out.

How Much to Breathe

Oxygen consumption. The amount of air which has to be moved in and out of the lungs depends on the amounts of oxygen and carbon dioxide to be transferred. These amounts depend mainly on how much work we are doing. The rate of *oxygen consumption* is one of the best indications of the amount of work being done. Some average figures may interest you. They are in liters, but a liter is almost the same thing as a quart.

TABLE V
Average Rates of Oxygen Consumption

Activity	Average Consumption
Basal—just "staying alive"	0.25 liters/min.
Quiet sitting	0.4
"Light" work—up to	1.0
"Moderate" work—up to	2.0
"Heavy" work—up to	3.0
"Exhausting" work—up to	4.0

The last figure applies to a man in good athletic shape; a lot of us wouldn't be able to hit three without really knowing it. A top-grade athlete may get up to 5.0 for a while. Every man has his top—his blood won't circulate fast enough beyond a certain point to carry any more.

The body does not have any real reserve of oxygen; but it does have a mechanism by means of which it can build up an oxygen debt. This lets us work beyond our maximum rate for short periods in emergencies and consume the necessary oxygen later.

Where does swimming under water fit into the oxygen consumption picture? The Experimental Diving Unit did a study on the subject and got these average values in experienced swimmers:

TABLE VI
AVERAGE OXYGEN CONSUMPTION OF EXPERIENCED SWIMMERS

Swimming Activity	Average Consumption
Resting under water (just sitting quietly)	0.33 liters/min.
0.5 knot swimming (painfully slow)	0.8
0.85 knot swimming (about average)	1.4
1.2 knot swimming (too fast)	2.5

Carbon dioxide production. This is closely related to oxygen consumption, generally just slightly less.

Respiratory minute volume (RMV). This refers to the total amount of air taken in and blown out in the course of a minute in order to supply the oxygen and get rid of the carbon dioxide. As a *rough* rule of thumb, it amounts to about 20 times the oxygen consumption. So, in very round numbers, the amount of air you need under water would range somewhere between 7 liters a minute at rest and 50 liters a minute for fairly hard swimming. Average comfortable swimming would require about 28 liters per minute. This is a handy figure for rough calculations since 28 liters is about the same thing as *1 cubic foot.* Using such figures can be helpful in estimating the duration of your air supply and the like. However, individuals can vary quite a bit from these averages, so don't push the figures too far.

Rate of breathing and tidal volume. "Respiratory rate" (the number of breaths per minute) varies a great deal among individuals. Experimental Diving Unit (EDU) studies have shown rates between 5 and 30 during average swimming and between 2 and 20 during rest under water.

"Tidal volume" (the size of a single breath) can be determined by dividing the RMV by the rate. The maximum tidal volume would be equal to the man's *vital capacity*—the greatest amount of air that he can blow out after a maximal inspiration. The average vital capacity is around 5 liters, but this also varies quite a bit from man to man.

Regulation. The body's mechanisms for the control of breathing are interesting. There are special "Analyzers" which sense the oxygen and carbon dioxide levels and which can cause increases or decreases in breathing when the levels get out of line. At least at rest, the carbon dioxide sensing system is the main controller. The oxygen mechanism serves mainly as an emergency standby most of the time. There are also special reflexes which increase breathing during work. The whole thing is a very complicated interacting affair. It is not completely understood even after years of research; and diving throws some curves into it which are real puzzles at the moment.

Overexertion. You've probably noticed that one of the main things which will stop you when you are working too hard is just getting "all out of breath." The mechanisms which control breathing have some lag in them, so this feeling and the frantic panting which goes with it may not show up right away—not until you've already gone quite a way toward "knocking yourself out." When it catches up with you, you just have to stop for a while and catch up on your breathing.

Even on the surface, where you have free access to air, this state of affairs isn't exactly pleasant. Underwater, even with a good scuba, you may be a long way from getting all the air you need when this happens. This can be very unpleasant indeed, and for a beginner it can be downright terrifying. In fact, it may be one of the most frequent things which sets off the chain of events leading to drowning. And such overexertion doesn't have to be the result of some emergency, like getting caught in a strong current. It can happen from something as simple as trying to keep up with a better swimmer.

On the surface, most of us have some idea of what our limits are and can avoid going beyond them. It is a little hard to realize just how much the breathing resistance of scuba can cut down those limits. But it is a good thing to keep in mind.

Depth versus air and oxygen requirements. The body consumes oxygen on the basis of actual number of molecules rather than volume. Therefore, the rate of oxygen consumption does not change with depth in terms of the amount used out of an oxygen supply cylinder. This fact gives closed-circuit, oxygen-breathing apparatus, and other systems which merely supply the amount of oxygen actually consumed, a considerable advantage. The amount is not only much smaller (about $\frac{1}{20}$) than that involved in open-circuit supply, but there is no increase at depth.

The RMV will remain about the same regardless of depth; but the gas which the lungs take in is compressed at depth, so the number of molecules in each breath—and the amount drained from the cylinder—increases. For this reason, an open-circuit rig which is good for a couple of hours at the surface will last only about one hour at 33 feet, half an hour at 99 feet, and so on. It is true that there are a lot more oxygen molecules crammed into each breath at depth, but this doesn't make much difference. It still takes the same *volume* of gas to keep the carbon dioxide washed out.

Nothing to Breathe

Before carrying the "Something to Breathe" subject any farther, it would be a good idea to consider some of the aspects of being underwater without anything to breathe. This may be intentional, as in breath-hold diving, or quite unintentional, as in running out of air, failure of the scuba, or such things as losing the mouthpiece.

When there isn't anything to breathe, you have two alternatives: (1) Hold your breath. (2) Drown. This isn't just an attempt to be funny. Both possibilities are quite important!

BREATH-HOLDING IN SKIN DIVING

The pitfalls of holding your breath during ascent in scuba diving have been covered. What about the sort of gambit where you take a breath at the surface, go down, stay as long as you can, and come up again? Of course, you can't get air embolism or lung damage from that. The air just re-expands and refills the lungs. It can't very well overfill them unless you've had access to extra air somewhere below the surface. So we can leave that dismal angle behind.

Among the devotees of the "no scuba" branch of the sport, ability to hold your breath for a long time is quite an asset; and how to hold it longer is a hot topic.

The most popular method is *hyperventilation:* breathing more than you need for a while before submerging. This can extend the time considerably, and until recently it was considered a fairly safe procedure. If not carried to excess (more than a few extra breaths), it is probably all right unless you "push your limits" by trying to stay down beyond the point when a real desire to resume breathing develops. Excessive hyperventilation, however, is now regarded as a means of achieving *permanent* breath-holding.

Hyperventilation has little effect on the body's oxygen supply but "blows off" carbon dioxide from the normal stores. Breath-holding time is lengthened because CO_2 now takes longer to build up to its "breakpoint" level. During the longer breath-hold, the diver's oxygen level can fall to a low value before he realizes that he must return to the surface and resume breathing.

The oxygen level reached in this way would probably seldom be low enough to cause serious trouble were it not for two factors that have been spotlighted by recent research: (1) Exertion (like underwater swimming during the dive) not only causes oxygen to be used up faster but decreases the sensitivity of the CO_2 breakpoint mechanism. This permits the O_2 level to go even lower than it would otherwise. (2) When the diver finally starts up from depth and the pressure around him decreases, the drop in partial pressure of oxygen in his lungs may be sufficient to stop further uptake of oxygen completely. At the same time, the partial pressure of CO_2 in the lungs also drops, and this gives a false sense of relief from the need to breathe. It is not at all surprising that divers who try to push their limits, especially after hyperventilation, sometimes lose consciousness from lack of oxygen (anoxia) and drown before regaining the surface. This has become recognized as a fairly common cause of death in skin diving. Underwater distance swimming events and spear fishing competition seem a very poor idea, since they encourage divers to run this risk.

Breathing oxygen before a dive is an even more effective means of extending breath-holding time. If oxygen-breathing is combined with hyperventilation, spectacular durations are possible (close to fifteen minutes at rest, for example). Unfortunately, it appears that oxygen-breathing also upsets the normal breakpoint mechanisms and can be hazardous. Carbon dioxide poisoning, which can also cause unconsciousness under water, becomes possible. Like excessive hyperventilation, oxygen-breathing should be avoided.

Depth itself will prolong breath-holding time, probably because of the increased oxygen pressure involved.

Drowning. This is undoubtedly the most frequent cause of death in scuba diving. The scuba diver gets himself into much riskier spots from this standpoint than either an ordinary swimmer or the suit-and-helmet diver. He is all right as long as his apparatus functions and nothing else goes wrong; but drowning can be the end result of a big assortment of mishaps, including a lot of seemingly trivial ones.

Getting panicky in a rough spot is probably involved in most scuba drownings. There are ways out of almost every conceivable emergency if you have been *trained* in what to do and can keep your head. But the man who just puts the gear on and shoves off is asking for trouble; and diving all by yourself without a buddy is another way of courting disaster.

Anybody who swims or dives should see to it that he knows how to give artificial respiration by the mouth-to-mouth (or mouth-to-nose) method. This provides much better lung ventilation than the older procedures, can be used anywhere (even in the water), and requires no equipment. There is nothing complex about it, but getting the head and jaw into proper position is essential and requires a little practice.

NOT ENOUGH OXYGEN—ANOXIA

Not getting enough oxygen is one of the results of having "Nothing to Breathe," but it isn't quite the same thing. *Anoxia* can be defined as a *lack of sufficient oxygen in the tissues.* And when the tissues don't have enough oxygen, they stop functioning normally and will eventually die. The brain is the most sensitive part of the body as far as oxygen-lack is concerned. Unconsciousness can occur very rapidly, and the brain cells will die if a severe lack of oxygen goes on for more than a very few minutes.

Anoxia can come about in many ways, since getting oxygen from the air around us all the way into the tissues is quite a process. Anoxia will be the major difficulty in any disease or mishap which can block its uptake, transport, or use at any stage; and anoxia is the final cause of almost all deaths.

How can anoxia happen in diving? Fortunately, there aren't too many ways that anoxia can come about in diving, short of an accident like air embolism or drowning. The usual causes boil down to (1) not enough to breathe, or (2) not enough oxygen in what you breathe.

The first one can certainly produce anoxia; but not being able to get enough to breathe is usually perfectly obvious before anoxia has a chance to become serious. At least, that cause of anoxia does not sneak up on you.

Not having enough oxygen in what you breathe is a different matter, and its lack of obvious warnings is the main reason we are concerned about it. You may be helpless before you know anything is wrong.

Actually there are only a few ways in which this lack of oxygen in the breathing medium can happen in diving. With open-circuit gear charged with decent air, it just can't happen. It is not likely in *closed-circuit, oxygen-rebreathing equipment* either; but there are a couple of ways it *can* happen: (1) Charging the cylinder with something besides oxygen. (This doesn't seem likely, but it has been done.) (2) Failing to "purge" the nitrogen out of the system with oxygen before you start breathing on it. (This can happen surprisingly easily.)

Here's why purging the closed-circuit scuba (and your lungs) is important:

In this type of gear, you simply rebreathe oxygen to and from a breathing bag, putting it through a carbon dioxide absorbent on the way. You consume oxygen and put out carbon dioxide; and, since the latter is absorbed, the volume of the gas decreases in proportion to your oxygen consumption. When the volume gets down to the point where there is no longer enough in the bag for inspiration, you simply bleed more oxygen into the circuit from the supply cylinder. In some models, this happens automatically; but, in either case, having the breathing bag "go flat" is crucial.

So let's say you put on a unit of this type and don't purge. You will probably have around 6 liters of gas in the system—lungs, breathing bag, and so on. Not having purged, a good bit of this will be air, containing 80 per cent nitrogen. You might start out with a 50-50 nitrogen-oxygen mixture. This would give you

oxygen—3 liters

nitrogen—3 liters

In "average comfortable" swimming, remember, you would use up this amount of oxygen in about two minutes. But your average tidal volume (size of breath) probably wouldn't be much over 2 liters. The 3 liters of nitrogen would satisfy you completely as far as breathing is concerned. The breathing bag just wouldn't go flat. You wouldn't know that you were running out of oxygen unless your body itself warned you in some way, and it hardly ever would.

Another type of equipment in which anoxia can develop is the so-called *"mixed-gas" breathing apparatus*. This type of gear has to be used for some military purposes. In it, mixtures of nitrogen and oxygen or helium and oxygen are rebreathed intentionally. The equipment is provided with arrangements for keeping the percentages within safe limits; but failures can produce anoxia. Existing systems of this kind require very diligent maintenance and careful use to be safe; and for this reason they are not used any more than necessary even for military jobs. Anything on this order which comes out of somebody's home workshop is very likely to be a death trap, and some commercial efforts along these lines have been almost as bad.

What is "enough" oxygen? It's the "partial pressure" which counts. At the surface, with 1 atm. total pressure and about 20 per cent oxygen in air, we have 0.2 atm. partial pressure of oxygen. This is ample. You would have the same partial pressure if you were breathing 5 per cent oxygen at 99 feet—but you'd become anoxic if you tried to come up.

What happens in anoxia? The effects of low oxygen depend on just how low it is. It can get down to about 0.17 atm. (17 per cent at surface) without much of anything happening, but below that a number of difficulties start to show up.

The troubles we are most concerned about are so much like getting drunk that it is hardly necessary to go into details. They represent progressive depression of the brain and include such things as loss of ability to concentrate, inability to think clearly, loss of coordination, slowing of reflexes, and the like.

Along with this, there is usually a good bit of *euphoria*—the medical word for feeling as if everything is wonderful when it isn't. All in all, anoxia is usually *far* from unpleasant. You lose not only your ability to recognize that anything is wrong but also your ability to get concerned about anything—or to do anything constructive about it. And before very long, you are just plain unconscious.

You will become almost completely helpless at about 0.12 atm., and unconsciousness occurs if you are down to 0.10 atm. (10 per cent at surface) for any length of time. Below that, death isn't far off unless you're rescued.

But aren't there any warning signs—things you can recognize before it is too late? Frankly, unless you can recognize the "drunk" sensation before it gets too marked, there aren't any other reactions which will help much underwater. Pulse and blood pressure will increase, but who takes his pulse during a dive? Breathing picks up a little, but usually not enough to notice

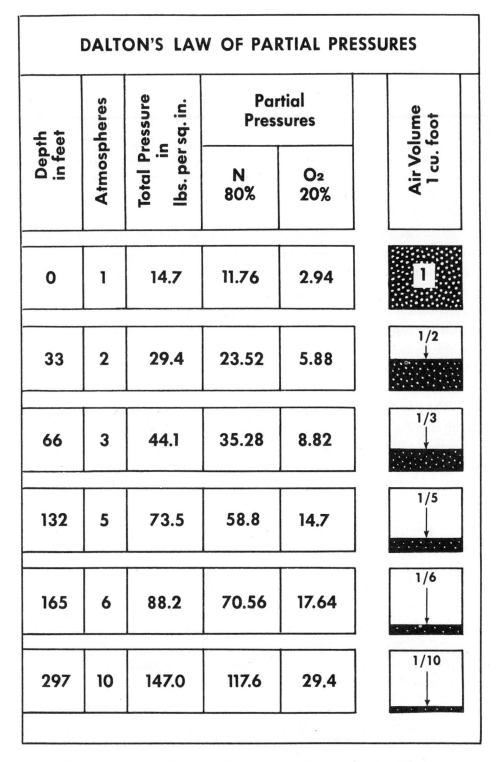

Depth in feet	Atmospheres	Total Pressure in lbs. per sq. in.	Partial Pressures		Air Volume 1 cu. foot
			N 80%	O₂ 20%	
0	1	14.7	11.76	2.94	1
33	2	29.4	23.52	5.88	1/2
66	3	44.1	35.28	8.82	1/3
132	5	73.5	58.8	14.7	1/5
165	6	88.2	70.56	17.64	1/6
297	10	147.0	117.6	29.4	1/10

FIG. 9. EFFECT OF DEPTH ON PRESSURE AND VOLUME OF GAS MIXTURE

until it is too late. You may get *cyanotic* (blue); but that is a poor warning even at surface, and who would see it underwater?

Treatment? If a victim of anoxia is fished out, treatment is not usually very hard to figure out; if he's breathing, just getting fresh air will usually bring him around. If he's not breathing, you'd naturally use artificial respiration. Oxygen is good if it's available; but it isn't usually essential; various medications, likewise.

Short of death, permanent brain damage is the main concern. Most victims who can be brought around fairly readily haven't much to worry about, even with some brain damage. A surprising amount of functional recovery may occur in time.

CARBON DIOXIDE EXCESS

How can it occur? Carbon dioxide intoxication is quite unlikely in *open-circuit scuba*. It might happen if the cylinders were charged with air containing carbon dioxide—rare, but worth keeping in mind. Another possibility is that the diver is simply not washing enough carbon dioxide out of his lungs because of insufficient breathing. For reasons unknown, some men tend to breathe inadequately when they are working at depth. This tendency can be aggravated by misguided efforts to "save air"—a process which appears to be potentially dangerous for this reason. Such problems can also be made worse by an excess of dead space in the breathing apparatus. (Dead space is defined as any part of a breathing system which catches expired air and gives it back on inspiration. Dead space apparently has to be fairly large to make much difference under ordinary conditions, but it should be kept as small as possible.)

Carbon dioxide buildup is much more likely in rebreathing rigs. The absorbent itself may get used up, be inactivated by getting wet, and the like. In a few such rigs—especially bargain and homemade articles—the absorption canister is just too small to start with, and anything like hard swimming will simply overload it. Some canisters will also "channel"—let carbon dioxide through, even though there is plenty of active absorbent.

How much is too much? Here again, it is partial pressure that counts. For example, breathing 5 per cent carbon dioxide at 33 feet gives the same effects as breathing 10 per cent at the surface—0.1 atm. in either case.

Talking in surface terms:

Up to 2 per cent	Not much happens.
Around 2 per cent	Increase in breathing normally starts.
At 5 per cent	There is considerable increase in breathing; normally noticeable and uncomfortable.

Up to 10 per cent	Progressive increase in breathing is noticeable, *plus* mental effects not unlike those of *anoxia*.
At 10 per cent and above	There are marked mental effects, eventual unconsciousness.

(Higher percentages—20 to 30 per cent or so—can cause a form of *convulsion* as well as unconsciousness.)

A few miscellaneous symptoms *may* show up in the milder exposures. These include: headache, a general "unwell" feeling, fatigue, weakness, mild twitches. (Most headaches come on *after* exposure.)

Death from carbon dioxide itself is a very rare thing; but losing consciousness from it underwater is certainly dangerous. Note that "10 per cent" is a crucial level in both carbon dioxide excess and anoxia.

To have a very uncomfortable increase in breathing before carbon dioxide levels become high enough to cause harm is the *normal* state of affairs. But *not everybody* will have this kind of response. A few can get into serious mental depression without knowing that anything is wrong—which makes carbon dioxide excess as dangerous for them as anoxia is for most people.

"*Shallow water blackout.*" Occasionally, a diver—usually one using an oxygen-rebreathing rig at moderate depth—will simply pass out without any warning whatever. This accident plagued the British during the war. It became less frequent after carbon dioxide absorption canisters were improved, but it still happens occasionally. EDU (Experimental Diving Unit) has seen a few cases. Just exactly what happens to these men has never been proved 100 per cent, but it is probably most often an example of failure to have a sufficient respiratory warning in carbon dioxide buildup, as mentioned above.

CARBON MONOXIDE POISONING

This can result from contamination of the air used for charging scuba. Such contamination can be caused by (1) engine exhaust gas getting into compressor air intake—a real possibility with gasoline-driven compressors; (2) "flashing" of lubricating oil in the cylinders of oil lubricated compressors, causing incomplete combustion of the oil.

For this reason, and because of the possibility of getting air which is loaded with oil vapor, it pays to be sure where your air comes from. Air from anything but a sure source should be checked for both carbon monoxide and oil vapor. A small, pocket-sized carbon monoxide tester can be a big help where you can't be sure.

The effects of carbon monoxide are very similar to those of anoxia. It is basically an anoxic condition since carbon monoxide combines with hemoglobin and keeps it from transporting oxygen. Symptoms like headache and feeling sick sometimes occur, but they are not reliable warnings.

The safe limits for carbon monoxide in air for diving have not been established. It is not certain how much the ambient pressure has to do with the toxicity of carbon monoxide. But it obviously pays to be on the safe side. For example, the University of California has fixed an upper limit of 10 parts per million (0.001 per cent) for air used by its diving activities.

*   *   *   *

So far, "Something to Breathe" has mostly been a discussion of quantities, what happens when you don't have anything to breathe, and things like anoxia and carbon dioxide excess.

Actually, aside from avoiding those difficulties, you haven't a lot of choice about what to breathe; but the question is worth a few words. It will be much easier to handle after we've discussed "Indirect Effects of Pressure," so we'll hold it until then.

Indirect Effects of Pressure

The "indirect," or "secondary," effects of pressure are almost purely physiological and not mechanical. They depend, not on the ambient pressure itself, or on differentials, but on the resultant partial pressures of the various gases which are present in whatever the diver is breathing. We already verged on this subject when we found that "partial pressure is what counts" in both anoxia and carbon dioxide excess.

The indirect pressure-effects can be discussed best under the headings of the gases concerned.

NITROGEN

Air contains about 79 per cent nitrogen, and so the partial pressures of nitrogen encountered at depth can be quite high. They have two important effects:

Nitrogen narcosis. This phenomenon has been known for a long time and has set the practical depth-limit for air diving at 300 feet or less. Cousteau and his associates, who seem not to have known about this before they ran into it, called this "Rapture of the Depths." This term is both descriptive and poetic, but it is likely to nauseate experienced divers.

The effects of nitrogen under pressure are very similar to those of a variety of gases used in *anesthesia*, and it is fairly well established that nitrogen has the same properties they do although in much weaker form. You can get a very good idea of how nitrogen narcosis feels by going to a dentist and having nitrous oxide for a tooth extraction.

The effects can also be compared to something a lot more familiar: alcoholic intoxication. There are differences; but being drunk, being anoxic, and having nitrogen narcosis have much in common. The relationship to alcohol has been expressed in what might be called Martini's Law: The mental effects of each additional 50 feet of depth, breathing air, are approximately equivalent to those of one dry Martini, assuming the stomach to be empty.

FIG. 10. NITROGEN NARCOSIS

Just as in the case of nitrous oxide and Martinis, individual susceptibility varies considerably. There are some who continue to carry on fairly nobly even after most of the others have slid under the table. There are a few who are pretty obviously "looped" as shallow as 100 feet. And, of course, there are also some who can be quite far gone without knowing it—"I've only had tee Martoonies," etc.

Incidentally, "tee Martoonies" equals 100 feet according to the above law. At that depth, you may not notice any impairment unless you try to do something which requires quick thinking or accuracy of thought or motion, like trying to read a depth gauge, figure decompression, or handle an emergency. In such cases, narcosis will be pretty apparent in most people. It is very important to realize that you are likely to be half shot in spite of feeling just dandy.

Experienced divers realize that they can barely be trusted to come in out of the rain once they get much below 200 feet—scarcely remembering what job they went down to do, caring less, and actually being a menace to themselves.

One of the best stories illustrating this fact, possibly true, is about a diver who was at 250 feet or so and obviously accomplishing nothing in spite of the blue stream of profanity which issued from the topside phone. When his tender finally got a word in edgewise and asked what he was doing and what was the matter, the drunken voice replied that his air hose was getting in the way something awful but not to worry because he had about gotten the ———— thing cut off. The diver was hauled up.

Whether it's true or not, this story has several morals. One of these has to do with the difference between air hose and scuba diving: the scuba diver doesn't have anybody on the other end of a telephone cable at the surface to keep track of him, keep him in contact with reality, and bring him up if worse comes to worst. And he doesn't have the protection of that clumsy, but sometimes very welcome, suit and helmet. If he feels like handing his mouth-piece to a passing fish—an impulse Cousteau mentions—he can. And if he drops this mouthpiece he may or may not have the wit to get it back in and cleared.

All this brings up a question: If a conventional diver doesn't generally trust himself at much over 200 feet, how deep should a scuba diver go? Perhaps you can form some conclusions of your own. No matter what record somebody finally sets for air diving with scuba, the deeper stuff remains largely useless and pretty uniformly foolish.

Helium has much less narcotic effect than nitrogen. For this reason, helium-oxygen mixtures are used in place of air for deep diving. (The oxygen content of such mixtures is reduced below that of air to avoid oxygen poisoning.) At what depth narcosis will become a problem with helium is not yet known. Some authorities believe that dives much beyond 1,000 feet will be impractical for this reason. (The role of CO_2 in narcosis is discussed on page 78.)

The duration of gas supply becomes such a limiting factor at greater depths that use of helium-oxygen mixtures in open-circuit scuba could rarely be practical. Hose-supplied systems with reuse of the gas mixture or the more complex types of mixed-gas scuba are required.

Decompression sickness. "Why decompress?" When the body is exposed to an increased partial pressure of any gas, considerable amounts of that gas will go into solution in the blood and tissues. The gas gets in by diffusion across the lung membrane which separates the alveolar gas from the blood flowing through the lungs. This blood becomes charged with the gas and then transports it to the tissues.

As long as the body remains exposed to elevated ambient pressure, gases taken up in this way will remain in solution. When the pressure is reduced, the gases will start coming out the same way they got in: through the blood and lungs. But for all the dissolved gas to get out in this way takes time; and, if the outside pressure is decreased too rapidly, the unloading process will get seriously behind. The partial pressure of the tissue gas can get quite far above the total pressure (outside, or ambient pressure), and a state called *supersaturation* will exist. Some supersaturation can be tolerated; but if it gets beyond a certain point, the gas will start to form bubbles.

Oxygen rarely gives any trouble this way because the tissues use it up fast enough to keep it from supersaturating. But the "inert" gases like nitrogen and helium—which the body does not use up in any way—can cause quite a bit of difficulty.

Opening a bottle of ginger ale makes a good demonstration of this process. There, the gas happens to be carbon dioxide; but the principle is the same. Before the cap comes off, the liquid holds the gas without any trouble because the whole works is under pressure. But taking the cap off drops the pressure, and the liquid becomes supersaturated and starts to bubble.

In bringing a diver up, the idea is to keep the degree of saturation from becoming great enough to cause bubbles. The guide for managing this is the *decompression table.* Its specified stops and the prescribed rate of ascent give time for enough gas to escape through the lungs to prevent trouble—usually.

Because some degree of supersaturation is tolerated, no stops at all are required for the shallower and shorter types of dive. A look at the table on page 210 shows this. That table is the one for standard decompression (stops made in the water on ascent) following dives on air. It is one of the decompression tables developed by the Navy (1958) and incorporated in the *U.S. Navy Diving Manual.**

It represents a great improvement over tables previously used and should cover most of the needs of scuba divers. The Diving Manual also provides decompression tables for longer and deeper air dives, for surface decompression (use of a recompression chamber for some or all of the stops), and for decompression following helium-oxygen dives. These other tables will seldom if ever be needed by sportsman divers, but one additional set of tables (provided) may be of considerable value for some: the system for determining proper decompression for *repetitive* dives (see discussion below).

Of greatest interest to most scuba divers are the "no decompression"

* *U.S. Navy Diving Manual,* NAVSHIPS 250-538, available from Superintendent of Documents, U.S. Government Printing Office, Washington, D.C. 20402 ($3.25).

limits specified by the standard air table: the times that can be spent in dives to various depths without having to make decompression stops on ascent. The following table summarizes these limits:

TABLE VII
"No Decompression" Limits

Depth (feet)	Bottom Time (minutes)
(less than 33)	(no limit)
35	310
40	200
50	100
60	60
70	50
80	40
90	30
100	25
110	20
120	15
130	10
140	10
150 to 190	5

"Bottom time" is the total elapsed between leaving the surface and starting ascent—not just time spent at the maximum depth. Note that it would rarely be possible to make a dive to 150 feet or more, accomplish any useful work there, and be ready to start up—all within five minutes; so attempting to make such deep dives on a "no decompression" basis is seldom advisable.

BE SURE TO UNDERSTAND these important points about use of the decompression table and "no decompression" limits:

1. *Depth* is tabulated in 10-foot steps. Unless your depth corresponds exactly to one of these tabulated depths (and you must be sure of this), use the *next greater* depth in selecting your decompression schedule. Example: a dive to 91 feet requires decompression according to a 100-foot schedule.
2. *Bottom time* means the number of minutes that elapse from the moment you leave the surface to the moment you start your ascent—*not* just the time actually spent on the bottom. Times are tabulated in 5- or 10-minute steps, and unless your time is exactly equal to one of the tabulated times, you must use the *next greater* one. Example: a 26-minute dive to 102 feet requires use of the schedule for 30 minutes at 110 feet.

NOTE: If a dive involves exceptional cold or hard work, add a safety factor by using the schedule for the depth or time (or both) beyond that which would normally be used.

3. *Rate of ascent.* The table was calculated and tested for an ascent rate of 60 feet per minute (one foot per second), and this should be followed. If you come up faster, you are omitting some of the decompression that ascent at the specified rate provides. If you come up slower, this amounts to spending more time at depth (and thus taking up more nitrogen) than was expected. If your dive was at all close to the stated depth and time of the schedule you are using, either mistake might result in decompression sickness.

4. *Repetitive dives* are defined as successive dives made within a twelve-hour period. Every dive, whether it requires decompression stops or not, leaves some excess of nitrogen in the body. This leaves gradually while you are at the surface, but it is not completely cleared out in less than twelve hours. Therefore, if you make another dive within a twelve-hour period, your body will contain more nitrogen when you start up from that dive than it would have if the previous dive(s) had not been made. As a result, you will need more decompression—or will be able to spend less time at depth on a "no decompression" basis.

The Diving Manual provides a system for safe and sensible determination of limits and decompression schedules for repetitive dives, giving "credit" for nitrogen lost during the time at surface between dives. The old rule of adding the bottom times of all dives made during the past twelve hours and using the depth of the last dive usually yielded much more decompression or much more restrictive limits than were necessary; but in some cases, it was not even safe.

Having to make decompression stops on ascent obviously makes scuba diving a lot more complicated, especially when there is a chance of running out of air during the stops, as is often the case. So, unless there is a very good reason for doing otherwise, the scuba diver is very much better off to stay within the "no decompression" limits and to make sure that he does not unwittingly go beyond those limits by making repetitive dives.

When it comes to diving in the decompression range, the suit-and-helmet diver has a lot of advantages: unlimited air supply; tenders who keep track of his time, depth, and stops. Proper decompression can be accomplished with scuba, but it entails more planning and preparation and more attention to details than most scuba divers are willing to put into it. Mistakes are easier to make and more likely to be serious. For any dive requiring decompression, an added margin of safety can be provided by a five-minute stop at the first decompression stage below that recommended by the tables for that particular set of circumstances.

A lot of people have either or both of two serious misconceptions about decompression in scuba diving. One is that you will always run out of air

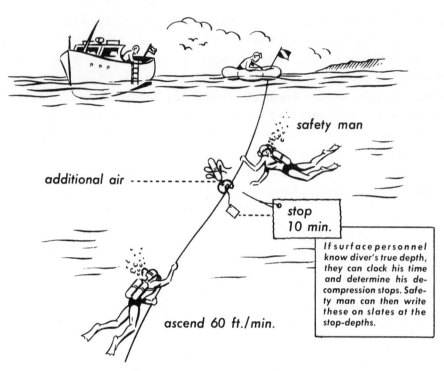

safety man

additional air

stop
10 min.

If surface personnel know diver's true depth, they can clock his time and determine his decompression stops. Safety man can then write these on slates at the stop-depths.

ascend 60 ft./min.

FIG. 11.   DECOMPRESSION STOPS

before you can get into decompression trouble. This is not true even with single-cylinder rigs; and it is very untrue with the larger models. The other misconception is that the decompression table is so unnecessarily conservative that you hardly have to bother about it. Though it is true that you *can* get away with violating it, if you are lucky and don't try it too often, it is not 100 per cent safe in the total picture. For instance, any Navy outfit which does a lot of diving will see its share of bends even if it sticks to the table religiously. With scuba, you are rarely in position to treat these cases properly as most Navy diving activities are.

Symptoms of decompression sickness. The most frequent manifestation of decompression sickness is *pain.* Usually, it is confined to one particular area of the body. Most often, pain shows up in a joint; and the legs are most often affected. However, the pain may be almost anywhere.

Very frequently, a diver will itch after a dive. Sometimes he will have a rash with the itch. This rash may be no more than a few red spots, or it can progress to a corpselike mottling. Unusual fatigue is another fairly frequent thing after diving, and it is usually regarded as the result of bubbles somewhere. Itch, rash, and fatigue may occur alone, together, or with pain or other symptoms. Sometimes they precede a more serious symptom, so a diver with any one of them should be watched very closely. Itch, rash, and fatigue generally disappear without requiring treatment; but if a rash becomes very severe, recompression should be considered. Progressive swelling occasionally occurs and may require treatment.

A diver who has a real bends pain isn't likely to call it a "mild" symptom. However, there are some symptoms—fortunately less frequent than pain—which are really serious. These are produced by bubbles in the *central nervous system* (brain and spinal cord) or in the *lung*. The lung symptoms are called "chokes." They may involve such things as shortness of breath, pain on deep breathing, coughing, and the like and should be given very prompt treatment.

The central nervous system symptoms can include a great variety of disorders. The following list will give some idea of the possibilities:

> Dizziness
> Weakness or paraysis anywhere in the body
> Numbness—loss of sensation anywhere
> Collapse and loss of consciousness
> Blindness or other disorders of vision
> Ringing of the ears or other defects of hearing
> Convulsions

Any of these indicates that some part of the nervous system has been deprived of its blood supply or has been "knocked out" by pressure from a bubble in the tissue itself. Because nerve tissue can't survive such insults for very long, treatment has to be prompt, and is automatically given on one of the longer treatment tables. These things, incidentally, can occur after perfectly ordinary dives with supposedly adequate decompression. In fact, EDU has at times seen more nervous system bends than the "pain only" type during its work in the *scuba range* of depths and times, even with ample decompression.

The possible variety of symptoms of decompression sickness is so great that almost any abnormality which shows up after a dive has to be considered a possible "bend" unless it is obviously caused by something else. The "obviously due to something else" idea can be misleading. For instance, a diver who develops a sore knee after a dive may know that he hit it on a rock during the dive—but such injuries may favor development of a bend in the affected location. The fact that a dive was within the "zero decompression" limits or that proper decompression was given doesn't mean very much, either.

Even an experienced diving medical officer may have a tough time deciding whether a certain symptom is due to decompression sickness or not. Frequently, a "test of pressure" has to be given; and, if this is inconclusive, the patient may have to be treated just to be safe.

Almost every bend, if untreated, will produce permanent injury of some degree. Whether this will be negligible or serious depends on the location and severity of the case. The disability may not show up at once either.

There are two *commandments* about decompression sickness: (1) remember that almost anything can happen; and (2) when in doubt, treat, and treat adequately.

In connection with the latter, prompt treatment of a doubtful or minor case—usually on a short table—will often save having to give long-table treatment, and possibly a bad result later.

Treatment. A copy of the Navy's standard treatment tables has been included (see page 69). Note that the basic principles involved in deciding which table to use are quite simple.

Unfortunately, many of the decisions which look simple on paper are not so simple in practice. Knowing when relief is complete is one of the biggest problems especially in neurological cases. Anybody can treat a routine case, but there are many times when there is no substitute for the experience and judgment of a diving medical officer—and there are also some times when he will have his fingers crossed along with everybody else.

The approximate total time of these various tables may be of interest:

TABLE VIII

APPROXIMATE DECOMPRESSION TIME OF THE NAVY STANDARD TREATMENT TABLES

Table	Time (hours)
1	2½
1A	6
2	4
2A	11
3	19
4	36½ to 38

This should make it obvious that treatment is far from being just a matter of going down until you feel better and then coming back up. Doing that is almost guaranteed to make you much worse off than you were before. The bubble must not only be squeezed to harmless size but also put back in solution. Inadequate treatment may leave the bubble where it is and load the patient with additional nitrogen.

Note the great saving of time which results from using oxygen in Tables 1 and 2 as opposed to 1A and 2A. This is because breathing oxygen greatly hastens the elimination of inert gas. Unfortunately, using it involves some risks. Someone must always be with the patient when oxygen is used.

It should be quite obvious that trying to give adequate treatment for decompression sickness by "water recompression" with scuba would be very difficult if not impossible. Knowing the location of the nearest chamber and having a means of getting to it in a hurry is almost as important in decompression sickness as it is in air embolism.

TABLE IX

Treatment of Decompression Sickness and Air Embolism*

Stops	Bends—Pain only		Serious Symptoms
Rate of descent—25 ft. per min. Rate of ascent—1 minute between stops.	Pain relieved at depths less than 66 ft. Use table 1—A if O_2 is not available.	Pain relieved at depths greater than 66 ft. Use table 2—A if O_2 is not available. If pain does not improve within 30 min. at 165 ft. the case is probably not bends. Decompress on table 2 or 2—A.	Serious symptoms include any one of the following: 1. Unconsciousness. 2. Convulsions. 3. Weakness or inability to use arms or legs. 4. Air embolism. 5. Any visual disturbances. 6. Dizziness. 7. Loss of speech or hearing. 8. Severe shortness of breath or chokes. 9. Bends occurring while still under pressure.
			Symptoms relieved within 30 minutes at 165 ft. — Use table 3 / Symptoms not relieved within 30 minutes at 165 ft. — Use table 4

Pounds	Feet	Table 1	Table 1-A	Table 2	Table 2-A	Table 3	Table 4
73.4	165	--------	--------	30 (air)	30 (air)	30 (air)	30 to 120 (air)
62.3	140	--------	--------	12 (air)	12 (air)	12 (air)	30 (air)
53.4	120	--------	--------	12 (air)	12 (air)	12 (air)	30 (air)
44.5	100	30 (air)	30 (air)	12 (air)	12 (air)	12 (air)	30 (air)
35.6	80	12 (air)	12 (air)	12 (air)	12 (air)	12 (air)	30 (air)
26.7	60	30 (O_2)	30 (air)	30 (O_2)	30 (air)	30 (O_2) or (air)	6 hrs. (air)
22.3	50	30 (O_2)	30 (air)	30 (O_2)	30 (air)	30 (O_2) or (air)	6 hrs. (air)
17.8	40	30 (O_2)	30 (air)	30 (O_2)	30 (air)	30 (O_2) or (air)	6 hrs. (air)
13.4	30	↓ 5 (O_2)	60 (air)	60 (O_2)	2 hrs. (air)	12 hrs. (air)	First 11 hrs. (air) Then 1 hr. (O_2) or (air)
8.9	20	5 (O_2)	60 (air)	↓ 5 (O_2)	2 hrs. (air)	2 hrs. (air)	First 1 hr. (air) Then 1 hr. (O_2) or (air)
4.5	10	↓	2 hrs. (air)	5 (O_2)	4 hrs. (air)	2 hrs. (air)	First 1 hr. (air) Then 1 hr. (O_2) or (air)
Surface		↓	1 min. (air)	↓	1 min. (air)	1 min. (air)	1 min. (O_2)

Time at all stops in minutes unless otherwise indicated.

* From *U.S. Navy Diving Manual.*

TABLE X

Notes on Recompression*

Explanation: All references to TABLES *indicate parts of Table IX, "Treatment of Decompression Sickness and Air Embolism."*

1. *General Considerations*
   a. Follow TREATMENT TABLES (table 1–21) accurately.
   b. Permit no shortening or other alteration of tables except on advice of trained *diving medical officer* or in extreme emergency.

2. *Rate of Descent in Chamber*
   a. Normal rate is 25 feet per minute.
   b. Serious symptoms: rapid descent is desirable.
   c. If pain increases on descent: stop, resume at a rate tolerated by patient.

3. *Treatment Depth*
   a. Go to full depth indicated by table required.
   b. Do not go beyond 165 feet except on decision of medical officer.

4. *Examination of Patient* (see article 1.6.2(14))
   a. If no serious symptoms are evident and pain is not severe, examine thoroughly before treatment.
   b. If any serious symptom is noted, do not delay descent for examination or for determining depth of relief.
   c. In "pain only" cases where relief is reported before reaching 66 feet, make sure it is complete before deciding on TABLE 1.
   d. On reaching maximum depth of treatment, examine as completely as possible to detect
      1) Incomplete relief
      2) Any symptoms overlooked
      NOTE.—At the very least, have patient stand and walk length of chamber.
   e. Recheck before leaving bottom.
   f. Ask patient how he feels before and after coming to each stop and periodically during long stops.
   g. Do not let patient sleep through changes of depth or for more than an hour at a time at any stop. (Symptoms can develop or recur during sleep.)
   h. Recheck patient before leaving last stop.

5. *Patient Getting Worse*
   a. Never continue bringing a patient up if his condition is worsening.
   b. Treat as a *recurrence during treatment* (see 6).
   c. Consider use of helium-oxygen as breathing medium for patient (see 8).

6. *Recurrence of Symptoms*
   a. *During* treatment:
      1) Take patient to depth of relief (but never to less than 30 feet; and not deeper than 165 feet except on decision of medical officer).
      (If recurrence involves serious symptom not previously present, take patient to 165 feet.)

MOST FREQUENT ERRORS RELATED TO TREATMENT

1. Diver's failure to report symptoms early.
2. Failure to treat doubtful cases.
3. Failure to treat promptly.
4. Failure to recognize serious symptoms.
5. Failure to treat adequately.
6. Failure to keep patient near chamber after treatment.

---

6. *Recurrence of Symptoms*—Continued
   a. *During* treatment—Continued
      2) Complete the treatment according to TABLE 4.
   b. *Following* treatment:
      1) Recompress to depth giving relief.
      2) If depth of relief is less than 30 feet,
         a) Take to 30 feet.
         b) Decompress from 30-foot stop according to TABLE 3.
      3) If relief occurs deeper than 30 feet,
         a) Keep patient at depth of relief for 30 minutes.
         b) Complete remaining stops of TABLE 3.
         NOTE.—If original treatment was on TABLE 3, use TABLE 4.
      4) Examine carefully to be sure no serious symptom is present. If the original treatment was on TABLE 1 or TABLE 2, appearance of a serious symptom requires full treatment on TABLE 3 or TABLE 4.

ALWAYS KEEP DIVER CLOSE TO CHAMBER FOR AT LEAST 6 HOURS AFTER TREATMENT. (Keep him for 24 hours unless very prompt return can be assured.)

7. *Use of Oxygen*
   a. Use oxygen wherever permitted by tables unless
      1) Patient has not had oxygen tolerance test, or
      2) Is known to tolerate oxygen poorly.
   b. Be sure mask fits snugly.
   c. Take all precautions against fire (see table 1–29).
   d. Tend carefully, being alert for symptoms of oxygen poisoning such as
      1) Twitching   3) Nausea
      2) Dizziness   4) Blurring of vision
   e. Know what to do in event of convulsion. Have mouth-bit available.
   f. If symptoms appear, remove mask at once.
   g. If oxygen breathing must be interrupted—
      1) On TABLE 1, proceed on TABLE 1–A.
      2) On TABLE 2, proceed on TABLE 2–A.
      3) On TABLE 3, continue on TABLE 3 using air.
   h. At medical officer's discretion, oxygen breathing may be resumed at 40-foot stop. If this is done, complete treatment as follows:
      1) Resuming from TABLE 1–A: breathe oxygen: at 40 feet for 30 minutes at 30 feet for 1 hour
      2) Resuming from TABLE 2–A: breathe oxygen: at 40 feet for 30 minutes at 30 feet for 2 hours
      3) In both cases, then surface in 5 minutes still breathing oxygen.
      4) Resuming from TABLE 3: breathe oxygen: at 40 feet for 30 minutes at 30 feet for first hour (then finish treatment with air)

---

*From *U.S. Navy Diving Manual.*

(Table X, Continued)

8. *Use of Helium-Oxygen*
   a. Helium-oxygen mixtures (ratio about 80:20) can be used *instead of air* (not in place of oxygen) in all types of treatment and at any depth.
   b. Use of helium-oxygen is especially desirable in any patient who
      1) Has serious symptoms that fail to clear within a short time at 165 feet.
      2) Has recurrence or otherwise becomes worse at any stage of treatment.
      3) Has any difficulty in breathing.

9. *Tenders*
   a. A qualified tender must be in chamber
      1) If patient has had any serious symptom.
      2) Whenever patient is breathing oxygen.
      3) When patient needs unusual observation or care for any reason.
   b. Tender must be alert for any change in patient, especially during oxygen breathing. (See 7, d–f.)
   c. *Tender must breathe oxygen* if he has been with patient throughout TABLE 1 or TABLE 2
      TABLE 1: Breathe oxygen—
         at 40 feet for 30 minutes
      TABLE 2: Breathe oxygen—
         at 30 feet for 1 hour
   d. Tender in chamber only through oxygen breathing part of TABLE 1 or 2 gains safety-factor by breathing oxygen for 30 minutes of last stop, but this is not essential. Tender may breathe oxygen during use of TABLE 3 or 4 at 40 feet or less.
   e. Anyone entering chamber and leaving before completion of treatment must be decompressed according to standard diving tables.
   f. Personnel outside must specify and control decompression of anyone leaving chamber and must review all decisions concerning treatment or decompression made by personnel (including medical officer) inside chamber.

10. *Ventilation of Chamber*
   (See art. 1.6.21, par. 18)
   Rule 1. Volume of air required (volume as measured at chamber pressure—applies at any depth):
   a. Basic requirement:
      1) Allow 2 cubic feet per minute per man.
      2) *Add* 2 cubic feet per minute for each man *not at rest* (as tender actively taking care of patient).
   b. When using oxygen:
      Allow 4 cubic feet of air *per man breathing oxygen* if this yields larger figure than basic requirement. (Do not add to basic requirement.)

Rule 2. Maximum interval between ventilations:
   a. Not using oxygen:
      Interval (min.)
      $$\frac{\text{Chamber (or lock) volume (cu. ft.)}}{\text{Basic vent. req. (cu. ft./min.) (from rule 1)}}$$
   b. Using oxygen:
      Interval (min.)
      $$\frac{\text{Chamber (or lock) vol. (cu. ft.)}}{\text{No. of men br. } O_2 \times 10}$$
   a. Timing of ventilation:
      1) Use any convenient interval shorter than maximum from rule 2.
      2) (Continuous steady-rate ventilation is also satisfactory.)
   b. Volume used at each ventilation:
      1) Multiply volume requirement (cu. ft./min.) from rule 1 by number of minutes since start of last ventilation.
   c. Use predetermined exhaust valve settings to obtain required volume of ventilation. (See article 1.6.21 (18), (b).)

11. *First Aid*
   a. First aid measures may be required in addition to recompression. Do not neglect them.
   b. See table 1–26 and *Standard First Aid Training Course*, NAVPERS 1–0081.

12. *Recompression in the Water*
   a. Recompression without a chamber is difficult and hazardous. Except in grave emergency, seek nearest chamber even if at considerable distance.
   b. If water recompression must be used and diver is conscious and able to care for himself:
      1) Use deep sea diving rig if available.
      2) Follow treatment tables as closely as possible.
      3) Maintain constant communication.
      4) Have standby diver ready.
   c. If diver is unconscious or incapacitated, send another diver with him to control his valves and otherwise assist him.
   d. If lightweight diving outfit or scuba must be used, keep at least one diver with patient at all times. Plan carefully for shifting rigs or cylinders. Have ample number of tenders topside and at intermediate depths.
   e. If depth is inadequate for full treatment according to tables:
      1) Take patient to maximum available depth.
      2) Keep him there 30 minutes.
      3) Bring him up according to TABLE 3 if he can tolerate exposure. (If patient has been taken beyond 100 feet, do not use stops shorter than those of TABLE 2–A.)

The U.S. Navy has had very favorable results with a new recompression procedure using lower pressure and employing oxygen-breathing throughout (except for short intermissions on air). If continued application of this method in certain naval establishments yields satisfactory results, it will probably become the standard procedure. It offers considerable saving of time over the present standard method of treating decompression sickness and air embolism.

Saturation diving. The need for prolonged decompression is one of the most serious limiting factors in diving to greater depths. Decompression time lengthens markedly as bottom time increases, but eventually the body becomes *saturated* with nitrogen (or helium) at the pressure of the depth. By this is meant that the inert-gas pressures in all the tissues have come to equilibrium with the external pressure of the gas, and no more will be taken up. The state of saturation is probably reached somewhere between twenty-four and forty-eight hours of exposure. Beyond the point of saturation, the decompression time needed on ascent will no longer increase. It will be very long, but presumably a diver who has reached that point would require no greater decompression time if he remained for a week or a month.

This is the basis of the "undersea habitation" idea being put into practice by Captain George Bond (U.S. Navy Sealab projects), Captain Cousteau (Conshelf stations), Mr. Edwin Link (Ocean Systems, Inc.), and others. The British Navy and some commercial groups are more inclined toward keeping the diver under pressure in a comfortable chamber at the surface and sending him to depth in a connecting submersible chamber. Actually living at depth, free of surface and weather problems, will become more attractive when an entirely independent source of power (such as a small nuclear reactor system) becomes completely practical. Even now, both approaches are very promising under appropriate conditions. For a great number of time-consuming jobs at depth, the long final decompression process will be vastly shorter than the combined decompression times of many short dives to the same depth.

HELIUM

Although helium has much less "narcotic" effect than nitrogen and is less dense and thus easier to breathe at depth, it presents almost the same problems as far as decompression is concerned. According to present U.S. Navy tables, decompression from a dive made with helium will often require more time than the same dive made with air. There is now reason to believe that some of the helium schedules that yield shorter times are not sufficiently safe.

Because of the depths involved, most saturation diving would be done with helium-oxygen mixtures. Because of the danger of oxygen toxicity (see below) in very long exposures, the partial pressure of oxygen would be kept close to that of air at the surface. For example, a mixture for use at 20 atmospheres might contain only 1 per cent oxygen.

Practical problems with helium (in addition to its cost) include the change in voice that it produces because of the faster speed of sound in helium. Normal voice-communication becomes almost impossible. High thermal conductivity leads to added problems in maintaining normal body temperature.

(More information about gases and mixtures will be found on page 77.)

OXYGEN

Can oxygen be harmful? Oxygen is essential to life, and increased amounts of it are beneficial in many types of disease. It may be hard to believe that such a gas could ever be harmful, but it is important for divers to realize that it very definitely can.

Even at the surface, breathing over 60 per cent oxygen for a long enough time (usually many hours, or even days) can cause harm. This "low-pressure oxygen poisoning" is almost always confined to *lung* irritation. It rarely happens because it is difficult to get above 60 per cent oxygen with the usual means of giving oxygen.

The "Divers' Variety" of oxygen poisoning affects the brain and causes convulsions. It does not occur unless the *partial pressure* of oxygen is somewhere over one atmosphere. Just exactly what the crucial pressure is has not been determined, but it is between one and two atmospheres.

How can oxygen poisoning come about? Exposing yourself to more than one atmosphere of oxygen pressure can be managed by breathing 100 per cent oxygen anywhere beneath the surface; but breathing 100 per cent oxygen isn't the only way to do it. For example, breathing air at 5 atmospheres (132 ft.) would expose you to 1 atm. of oxygen; and breathing air at 10 atm. (297 ft.) would yield 2 atm. of oxygen. You could also get 2 atm. of oxygen by breathing 50 per cent oxygen at 99 feet, and so on.

The possibility of oxygen poisoning is usually associated with the use of *closed-circuit, oxygen-rebreathing apparatus.* Although this is the most frequent situation, it is certainly not the only possible one.

Open-circuit scuba presents virtually no chance of oxygen poisoning if it is charged with air and used at reasonable depths. Using oxygen (it is more available many places than good compressed air) or high-oxygen mixtures make it a very real possibility.

"Mixed-gas" scuba gear is not likely to be common among civilian enthusiasts for some time, but many a basement genius has something of the sort up his sleeve. It is likely to be a ripe source of oxygen poisoning if some of the schemes which are floating around get carried out. (See "What to Breathe.")

Whether oxygen poisoning will occur in any situation depends upon quite a number of factors:

1. The partial pressure of oxygen.
2. The duration of exposure.
   (The higher the oxygen pressure, the shorter the time, and vice versa.)
3. The amount of exertion.
   (Work can cut the safe time of exposure down to less than a tenth of what it would be at rest.)
4. Presence of excess carbon dioxide.
   (Even rather small amounts can speed up the onset of oxygen poisoning considerably.)
5. Individual differences—how susceptible the diver is.
   (Some are much more susceptible than others, and the same man's tolerance can vary quite a bit from day to day.)

All Navy divers who will be exposed to oxygen in their work are given an *oxygen tolerance test*. This involves breathing oxygen for 30 minutes at 60 feet at rest in a recompression chamber. Hardly anybody flunks the test, but it does happen. As a matter of fact, the average man is able to hold out for 2 hours under those conditions. By way of illustrating the effect of exertion, working moderately hard would cut the average tolerance down to 10 minutes or so.

The basic Navy rule about breathing oxygen on working dives under normal circumstances is this:

Do not breathe oxygen deeper than 25 feet.
Observe proper time limits (given below).

Where it is essential to use oxygen at deeper depths or for more than a short time, the limits of this table are applied:

TABLE XI

Time Limits for Breathing Oxygen at Deeper Depths

Depth (feet)	Time (minutes)
40	10
35	25
30	45
25	75
20	110
15	150
10	240

These limits apply to normal, moderate work and are generally safe for the average diver; but they do not allow for exceptional exertion, carbon dioxide excess, or unusual susceptibility to oxygen poisoning. And a depth-measurement error of a few feet could make quite a difference.

But what is oxygen poisoning? Nobody really knows exactly what is going on in the brain when oxygen poisoning happens. But the manifestation which causes real concern is *convulsion*. There may be other symptoms, but they appear to be preliminaries to convulsion rather than anything separate.

It is a little difficult to explain what a convulsion is; but if you have ever seen a real convulsion of any kind, you probably haven't forgotten what it looked like. By and large, all convulsions are about the same regardless of what caused them—epilepsy, high fever in a child, electric shock treatments in mental disease, or high oxygen.

Basically, a convulsion involves a severe disturbance in the brain which causes loss of consciousness and in which the brain areas which control the muscles are "firing" all out of control. At one stage (tonic) all the muscles will be contracting at once. The victim becomes rigid all over, breathing stops, the back may be arched, and so on. When the storm of activity begins to die down, the muscles are triggered more or less at random, and a phase of jerking and thrashing (clonic) sets in.

All of this lasts only a couple of minutes. A knocked-out phase (post-convulsive depression) follows. During this, the patient will be unconscious at first, later very restless and confused, and part of the time just asleep. This phase may last somewhere between 15 minutes and an hour. Then, usually, he will wake up and start asking what happened. He will be pretty tired and may have a headache, but that is usually about all.

The convulsion itself does not cause any demonstrable harm to the brain. Once in a while, a bone somewhere may give way under the terrific muscular strain, or the victim may chew his tongue in the process. But the real danger is in what may happen during the seizure. A scuba diver would very possibly drown.

Oxygen convulsions can start right out of the blue with no warning symptoms at all. But in quite a few cases there are certain things which can be recognized in time to let the diver get himself out of the situation. Reducing the oxygen partial pressure by coming up or by other means will very often keep the convulsion from happening if this is done soon enough. The warning symptoms which are most likely to show up, alone or in various combinations, are these:

1. Twitching.
   Most often, it starts first in the area around the mouth or eyelids, sometimes in the diaphragm (causing jerky breathing) or in working muscles.

2. Nausea.
3. Dizziness.
4. Ringing of the ears.
5. Visual disturbances.
   (Pipe-line vision is one of the most frequent.)
6. Mental disturbances.
   (These may include anxiety, irritability, confusion, and so on.)
7. Respiratory distress.
   (Shortness of breath, and so on.)

Note that some of these symptoms can come about for a variety of reasons other than oxygen poisoning. Some of them can show up in carbon dioxide excess or even *lack* of oxygen. Nausea could be due to things like nervousness or an unwise lunch. But any one of these symptoms, if definite, is potentially serious enough to warrant stopping the dive—whether it is caused by oxygen poisoning or not.

What can you do? There is really no treatment for oxygen convulsions, once under way. The important thing is to keep the victim from drowning or otherwise hurting himself during the fit. A convulsion will go through its course and then stop regardless of what is done in the meantime. Even if the victim continues to breathe oxygen, he will seldom have another convulsion for some minutes. It is far better to get him well in hand to make sure he can't drown than to be in a rush to "get the mask off."

This brings up a rather thorny problem: what to do with a diver who starts convulsing underwater? We can assume that you'd be using the *buddy system* and would be able to get to him fairly fast, but what then? Bringing him up during the breath-holding tonic phase could conceivably cause air embolism. But unless the man were in a rig where drowning was almost impossible, it would probably be best to follow your instincts and take him up, but not too fast.

After a convulsion is over, the big thing is to see that breathing resumes normally. Almost invariably, breathing movements will start all right—use artificial respiration if they don't—but the tongue may have fallen back or secretions may be obstructing the airway.

What to Breathe

Deciding what breathing medium to use in your scuba is seldom a problem. With open-circuit equipment, air is the only logical choice for normal use. With closed-circuit oxygen-rebreathing gear, oxygen is absolutely the *only* choice. But there are always so many questions about the possibility of breathing something different that the subject is worth a few words.

First of all, why not use oxygen in open-circuit gear? There are several good reasons:

1. Danger of explosion on charging.
   Oil and oxygen will cause explosion if they get together under pressure. Oil may have gotten into the gear either during manufacture or repair, or as a residue of oil vapor from a previous air charge.
2. Danger of oxygen poisoning.
   Use of oxygen imposes severe depth-time limits that are not normally associated with open-circuit gear.
3. There are absolutely no advantages.
   Oxygen does not decrease the amount of gas you use and you can't go deep enough to get any decompression advantage from it.

WHAT ABOUT "MIXTURES"?

Nitrogen-oxygen. Of course, air is a nitrogen-oxygen mixture. Its main drawback is the amount of nitrogen it contains and what this means in terms of decompression. The most obvious way to remedy this is to boost the amount of oxygen present. If you cut the nitrogen percentage in half (40 per cent nitrogen, 60 per cent oxygen), you could theoretically double your absolute depth as far as decompression limits are concerned. But the corresponding increase in oxygen pressure would stop you with oxygen poisoning long before you could take full advantage of this. The interrelationship between these limits becomes very complicated. This is especially true because the partial pressure of oxygen appears *not* to be the only basic factor determining oxygen tolerance in "mixture" breathing. This business is still under intensive study, and it hasn't yet been possible to define just what the oxygen limits in nitrogen-oxygen diving should be.

Even if this were all settled, using such mixtures in open-circuit scuba would hardly be worth the trouble of mixing and analyzing—or the expense of buying—the mixtures. The short duration of gas supply at depth would keep you from getting much of any benefit from the extension of depth-time limits.

Helium-oxygen. Granting that the breathing mixture has to contain oxygen and that the oxygen has to be diluted if you are going deep, the mixture question boils down to what you can use for dilution. Besides nitrogen, helium is about the only practical possibility.

Helium-oxygen diving, with a modified form of deep-sea rig, is a well-developed procedure in the Navy and is used for virtually all very deep diving. For most purposes, the only advantage of helium is its lack of anesthetic action at greater depths. In the scuba range, decompression takes longer with helium than with nitrogen—even when you follow the standard helium decompression procedure and breathe oxygen at all stops from 50 feet to the surface. This process, incidentally, could be quite an inconvenient and risky business with scuba; and it has to be done unless you want to compute and test new helium decompression tables.

With open-circuit scuba, helium presents the same problem of gas-supply duration versus any advantage you would get from using higher oxygen percentages to cut down the need for decompression.

Miscellaneous gases. Hydrogen has been used for diving, but the danger of explosion makes this a complex and touchy business. The hydrogen technique was developed in Sweden, where helium was not readily available. Hydrogen-oxygen does not seem to have any advantages over helium-oxygen, at least at depths thus far reached.

"Noble gases" other than helium have been tried (such as argon and krypton). Most appear to be more "narcotic" than nitrogen. Xenon is usable as an anesthetic gas at normal pressure. Neon appears suitable for deep diving but is far too expensive at present.

According to what is now known, any "inert" gas usable for diluting oxygen in diving will involve much the same decompression problems as nitrogen. The idea of using combinations of inert gases, or of alternating them, may have some merit. Claims that narcosis is really due to CO_2 and not to the inert gas itself appear unfounded, although a rise in the body's CO_2 level (as in "working beyond your breathing") can greatly accentuate narcotic effects, even to the point of causing unconsciousness.

BREATHING APPARATUS FOR "MIXED GAS"

As mentioned above, there is not much point in using nitrogen-oxygen or helium-oxygen mixtures in open-circuit scuba, and they absolutely must not ever be used in simple closed-circuit rigs (because of the danger of anoxia).

The drawback with open circuit is the limitation of gas-supply duration. This can be overcome by using a system in which part or all of the gas is *rebreathed.* But safe rebreathing of mixtures requires apparatus which is far more complicated than the simple oxygen-rebreathing circuit. The big problem is maintaining the proper proportions of gases in the mixture—so that you can steer clear of both anoxia and oxygen poisoning and keep the inert gas where it belongs from the standpoint of decompression. Although several types of "mixed gas" scuba exist, and are used for special military jobs, none of them is at all appropriate for "sports" type use. The great potential hazards of home-workshop versions of this kind of apparatus have already been mentioned. However, especially when the problem of safe oxygen limits for "mixture" diving is licked, perfected versions of "mixed gas" scuba should offer the greatest range of capabilities in self-contained diving.

ARTIFICIAL GILLS AND LIQUID BREATHING

The main known obstacles to diving to extreme depths lie in the effects of the inert gas required to dilute oxygen in the diver's breathing medium. The total pressure of the gas a diver breathes must be equal to the pressure that surrounds him. Oxygen must be included in that gas, but its partial pressure must be kept within safe limits; and the remainder of the gas pressure must be provided by an inert gas such as nitrogen or helium.

Fish are unaffected by oxygen poisoning and inert gas problems even at great depth because they are exposed only to the gas pressures that exist in the water. These in turn are essentially the same as in air at the surface. The total pressure of gas in a liquid, unlike that in a gas mixture, does not have to be equal to the ambient pressure. This fact has suggested that man might be able to go to very great depth if he could "breathe" a suitable liquid either with his own lungs or by circulating his blood through an artificial gill. Experiments to date suggest that such developments might someday be made practical but that many very serious problems must first be solved. In the meantime, we do not know at what depth the hydrostatic pressure itself may start to have unfavorable effects in man. It is possible that pressure itself will be an insuperable problem even at depths where gas-breathing is still acceptable. If so, the practical value of gills or liquid breathing might be very limited, even if they prove feasible.

4

FUNDAMENTALS OF COMPRESSED GASES AS RELATED TO SCUBA

The current popularity of scuba diving could not have been attained without the demand regulator. This regulator automatically supplies the diver, regardless of depth, with his requirements of gas in equilibrium with the surrounding water pressure.

Contents of Gases

Air is considered to be the safest gas and is the one which is used with open-circuit scuba equipment. The term "open-circuit" designates that the exhaled gases are discharged and not rebreathed. There may be some partial rebreathing equipment available, now or in the future, in which part of the exhaled gases are conserved for the next inhalation and part are discarded. In closed-circuit breathing, the same gas is breathed over and over. Sufficient oxygen is allowed to enter this system to replace that which has been consumed by the body, and the exhaled gases go through a canister containing a carbon dioxide absorbent to remove the carbon dioxide from the gas prior to the next inhalation. The closed-circuit systems are more complicated and require the use of oxygen, rather than air. In the open-circuit systems, there is no advantage to the use of oxygen, since we cannot absorb more than a small percentage (5 per cent) of the oxygen from the gas which we breathe and normally air (20 per cent oxygen and 80 per cent nitrogen) is more than adequate to supply our oxygen requirements. Also, there is the possibility of oxygen poisoning below the 25-foot level. The possibility of oxygen toxicity is approached as the partial pressure in the lungs nears the 2-atmosphere mark of oxygen pressure. In other words, if we were to breathe 100 per cent oxygen at the surface, the partial pressure would then be 100 per cent of the atmosphere, or 1 atmosphere. When we descend to 33 feet (2 atmospheres) the partial pressure of oxygen is then 2 atmospheres. Following the same pattern, this would mean that the limit would be:

% O_2 in Mixture	Depth Limit	Total (Pressure Atmospheres)	Equivalent O_2 Pressure
100	32	2	2
50	99	4	2
25	231	8	2
20	297	10	2
10	627	20	2

Greater precautions must be taken in the handling of oxygen equipment than are necessary with compressed air equipment.

Gas containing carbon dioxide or carbon monoxide in amounts beyond certain limits will cause poisoning. More detailed information on this subject is included elsewhere in this book. (See Chapter 3.) Limits generally acceptable are no more than 0.03 per cent for carbon dioxide (the equivalent of ordinary outdoor air) and 10 parts per 1,000,000 for carbon monoxide.

The nitrogen in air is inert and has little or no effect on the body except at a depth of approximately 100 feet. At greater depths, the excess pressure of this gas causes nitrogen narcosis, or "Rapture of the Depths." Mixed gases such as helium-oxygen are used at great depths to overcome this objection.

Since gases are compressible and water is not, there is a definite relationship between the volume of gas and the depth of water. Air at sea level is at 1 atmosphere of pressure or 14.7 psi. The air volume at a depth of 33 feet (2 atmospheres) is one half of the surface volume; at 66 feet (3 atmospheres) it is one third of the surface volume; and at 99 feet (4 atmospheres) it is one fourth of the surface volume.

Since our normal breathing requirements using scuba are approximately 1 cubic foot per minute at sea level and gas cylinder contents are expressed in cubic footage under one atmosphere of pressure at 70° F., it is easy to compute a timetable for any given size cylinder at any given depth. Thus, a 50-cubic-foot cylinder would give approximately 50 minutes of use at sea level; 25 minutes of use at 33 feet; 16 minutes at 66 feet; or 12 minutes at 99 feet. The requirements vary from person to person and will decrease at rest, or increase with strenuous exercise. However, the calculation above is a useful rule of thumb to follow.

Air or gas, then, is compressed on descent and expands on ascent. For example, a bubble having a volume of 3 cubic inches at 99 feet will enlarge to 4 cubic inches at 66 feet, 6 cubic inches at 33 feet, and 12 cubic inches at the surface. Observing these figures, it is apparent that the largest increase in bubble size per foot of ascent occurs between the 33-foot level and the surface. This means that the greatest danger from air embolism occurs in ascent from a relatively shallow depth. (Air embolism is discussed in Chapter 3.)

The Techniques of Filling Cylinders

Cylinders used for storing compressed gases are made in many sizes and to various specifications. The U.S. Bureau of Mines requires that all cylinders be registered with it by serial number, and the Interstate Commerce Commission requires that cylinder pressure ratings be stamped on the cylinders and that they be hydrostatically tested every five years. On the shoulder of the cylinder will appear a number of symbols. The cylinder manufacturer may have his initials or trademark stamped into the cylinder. The series of numbers by themselves indicates the serial number of the cylinder, and the numbers following the stamping ICC3A or ICC3AA indicate the working pressure for which the cylinder is approved. In addition to this number there will appear numbers indicating the month and year of the last hydrostatic test. Usual working pressures for cylinders are generally one of the following and are expressed in psia at 70° F. at sea level: 1,800, 2,015, 2,065, 2,215, 2,265, and 2,400. The ICC will permit cylinders to be filled to a pressure 10 per cent above these ratings. Commercial gas companies are not permitted to fill cylinders unless they are properly stamped and are within five years of the last hydrostatic test. There are cylinders imported from other countries and some surplus cylinders which do not meet these requirements and thus cannot be filled by the compressed gas companies. All cylinders must have a safety relief device either in the form of a bursting disk, generally set between 2,400 and 3,000 psi, and/or a fusible metal plug to melt out at between 130° and 160°. Cylinder valves and safeties should be disassembled or removed only by qualified service personnel.

Gas expands with heat and, of course, contracts with cold. The approximate rate of change is 5 pounds for each degree Fahrenheit of temperature. For example, a cylinder filled to a pressure of 2,000 pounds at 70° will have a pressure of 2,200 pounds at 110°, or 1,800 pounds at 30°. This has a direct application in scuba, since cylinders often lie in the sun and consequently show a gauge pressure considerably higher than will be shown when they are taken into the much cooler water.

To prevent having underfilled cylinders when they cool, the temperature of the cylinder must be taken into consideration at the time of filling. When a cylinder is filled, the gas in the cylinder is compressed to approximately 135 atmospheres. This, in turn, creates considerable heat. Consequently, the rate of filling must not be too rapid in order to avoid excessive temperature rises. The rate of filling must be slow enough that the hand can be held on the cylinder with no discomfort. Should the cylinder become hot, filling should be discontinued temporarily until it cools.

Since human life is at stake and dependent entirely upon the purity of the gas in the cylinder, every possible precaution must be taken against contamination. If a cylinder has a pressure of 50 pounds or more in it at the time it is to be filled, we can be reasonably sure that no contaminator has entered the cylinder. On the other hand, if the cylinder has less than 50 pounds, or has the valve open, it would be unsafe to assume that the residual contents of the cylinder are still pure enough for human consumption. A cylinder with the valve open will have breathed some of the surrounding atmosphere because of temperature changes and may have pulled in a contaminator such as carbon monoxide. Under these conditions, the cylinder must be either evacuated or purged before being filled for service. Compressed gas companies have vacuum pumps and are in a position to evacuate cylinders before filling. When filling cylinders from a cascade system, it is impossible to evacuate the contents of the cylinders. In this case, the cylinders should be filled to approximately 300 pounds and then this pressure blown off in order to insure the washing out of the residual gas that may have contained a contaminator. It is common practice to purge at least twice where there is any known contaminator. After the cylinder is thus purged, it can be filled in the normal manner.

There are available air compressors designed for the filling of these small cylinders. Generally speaking, these pumps will compress air at a rate between 0.3 and 1.5 cubic feet per minute. Thus, the filling time required is fairly long.

When using a compressor driven by a gasoline engine, be sure that the exhaust fumes are downwind from the intake side of the compressor and that there is proper filtering of the compressed air to avoid having exhaust fumes enter the cylinders. In the event an oil-lubricated compressor is used, similar precautions must be taken to prevent oil vapors from entering the breathing air cylinders. See Chapter 3 on "Medical Aspects of Diving" for reference to carbon monoxide, carbon dioxide, and oil vapors.

Some of the compressed gas companies manufacture compressed air in two grades. One is merely a compressed gas which may be used by air brush artists, for blowing out lines, or for cleaning such things as radiators. This compressed air is usually unfit for breathing and will generally have a different valve outlet from the air which is compressed for breathing purposes. When asking for compressed air for scuba use, be sure to state that you want it for breathing purposes.

CASCADE SYSTEM FOR RECHARGING SMALL BREATHING AIR CYLINDERS

An economical way of filling small cylinders is from a cascade system. This system utilizes several 300-cubic-foot cylinders, which are filled to a pressure of 2,400 pounds. Do not confuse these cylinders with 220- or 250-cubic-foot cylinders, which are filled only to pressures between 2,000 and 2,265 pounds.

General Instructions

A system utilizing only one or two large cylinders is neither practical nor economical for the recharging of small cylinders. In order to have efficiency in recharging, it is necessary to set up a bank of at least three large cylinders. (Little advantage can be gained with more than three or four.) These cylinders are manifolded together to the charging line for the small cylinder. The high pressure hose should include a bleed valve for relieving pressure after charging and before disconnecting the charged cylinder.

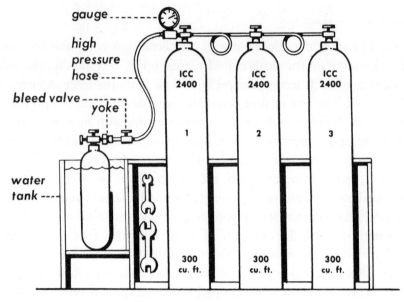

FIG. 12.   CASCADE SYSTEM

Note bottle rack for safety.

The procedure is to open one of the large cylinders and bring the pressure up to full pressure in the small cylinder, or until the pressure balances between the 300-cubic-foot cylinder and the small cylinder. After the first and second small cylinders are filled, this pressure may be down to 1,600 or less. In this case, the valve on the first large cylinder is turned off, and the valve on the second large cylinder is opened to utilize the higher pressure of the second large cylinder and thus bring the small cylinder up to the required pressure. After several small cylinders have been filled, it will become necessary to charge from cylinder No. 1 up to whatever the pressure may be, let us say 800 pounds, shut off No. 1 and charge from No. 2, which may bring the small cylinder up to, let us say, 1,400 pounds, then shut off No. 2 and top off with No. 3 to the required pressures.

When the pressure in No. 1 cylinder gets down to 300 pounds, it is impractical to use it any further, and the No. 1 cylinder should be replaced. Cylinder No. 2 now becomes No. 1, No. 3 becomes No. 2, and the fresh cylinder No. 3. By utilizing this system of three large, high-pressure cylinders, a recovery of approximately 80 to 85 per cent of the gas in the large cylinders can be made. If there are a large number of small cylinders to be filled, it is suggested that it may be practical to manifold more than three large cylinders together in order to get better efficiency.

Utilizing this three-cylinder manifold system to fill scuba cylinders will effect a saving of approximately 60 per cent over the cost of sending the individual cylinders into a plant for refill.

Detailed Instructions

The first step, after tightening all connections, is completely to open the valve and reserve on the small cylinder, then open, very slowly, the valve on large cylinder No. 1, letting the pressure flow from the large cylinder to the small cylinder. The rate of flow should be very slow in order to prevent over-heating of the small cylinder as the gas is recompressed into the small cylinder. It should take approximately 5 minutes to fill a small cylinder from the large cylinders. If they are filled at a faster rate, there is danger of overheating the small cylinder. In other words, the pressure increase in the small cylinder should not be over 100 pounds every 15 seconds. Should the small cylinder, at any time, get so hot that you cannot hold your hand on it, stop the filling process until the cylinder cools off. If a full 300-cubic-foot cylinder is being utilized, it will fill the first one or two small cylinders by itself.

Care should be taken not to allow excess pressure to flow into the small cylinder. The large cylinders are filled to a 2,400-pound pressure, and many of the small cylinders are limited to 1,800 or 2,000 pounds. The limiting pressure of the small cylinder is stamped into the metal of the cylinder. It will be found following the stamping ICC-3A or ICC-3AA. Thus, a cylinder of 1,800 pounds working pressure would be stamped ICC-3A-1800.

As soon as the small cylinder is up to pressure, or when the flow stops between the large and the small cylinder, the large cylinder should be turned off. The air going through the line makes a hissing sound which can easily be heard. After the pressure balances between the small and large cylinder, you can tell that the gas has stopped flowing because you will no longer hear the hissing sound. When additional pressure is required that is not obtainable from the cylinder No. 1, shut off the valve on cylinder No. 1, then open the valve on large cylinder No. 2 to bring the small cylinder up to pressure— or, in the event of a partially used large cylinder, until the flow of air stops, indicating that the pressure is in balance. The same process should be repeated with cylinder No. 3 until the small cylinder reaches the required pressure as indicated on the charging line gauge.

The valve on the small cylinder must be closed and the bleed valve opened prior to disconnecting any of the manifold lines. When disconnecting the filling line from the small cylinder, loosen the nut slowly to allow the high pressure in the filling line to escape before completely disconnecting the line.

To fill another small cylinder, start at the beginning and repeat the process.

For safety and temperature control it is desirable to have the scuba cylinder immersed in a cold water tank during filling.

5

BASIC SKIN AND SCUBA EQUIPMENT

Since the dawn of history on earth man has had to go into the water and sometimes under the water. From the time of Homer, Alexander the Great, Aristotle, and down through the centuries, men have been seeking ways to extend their diving time, ways to go deeper into the waters of the world.

During these centuries, except for the past decade, the primary objective of the diver was commercial or military. Because of this the equipment the divers used could be relatively expensive. The techniques of diving practiced then, as well as the equipment itself, required several men in a diving crew, yet diving was still economically feasible because it was being done for gain.

The sport diver receives no gain from the use of his equipment except the pleasure of its use and possibly a limited amount of food for his table. To him one of the primary considerations in the purchase of equipment is cost. Because of this factor and because of the very number of potential divers, the trend in diving equipment has been away from the complex and expensive helmet gear toward the less expensive and relatively less complex self-contained underwater breathing apparatus—scuba.

Scuba has opened up new fields for the commercial, open sea, research, and military diver. Contrary to a rather popular belief, the importance of scuba does not lie in the fact that it has replaced, or ever can replace, conventional helmet equipment. For certain types of underwater work helmet equipment will remain the best suited.

Self-contained diving equipment has long been used. The first such equipment was designed by William H. Jones in 1825. Basically this first scuba was a thin copper or leather helmet fitted with a window. To this was attached a short diving dress or suit, having elastic waist and armholes. Air was carried in an iron reservoir in the form of a cylindrical belt. The iron container was charged to about 450 psi, a terrific pressure for those days.

In the years since Jones pioneered scuba many advances have been made;

today's equipment does not remotely resemble that of the early nineteenth century. One can readily see the technological and fabrication advances by glancing at the advertisements in any of the diving magazines. One retail house presents 62 different masks, 30 kinds of snorkels, 104 sizes and styles of fins, 40 regulator models, 56 wet suit selections. These and many more supplementary items make basic selection a real chore. Following simple guidelines of fit, function, and adaptability will simplify the selection of basic equipment.

Skin Diving Equipment

An individual becomes skilled in surface and underwater swimming only after he has solved many problems. Even with the help of expert teachers he must ultimately solve these problems himself by experimentation and practice. Each piece of equipment used by the diver, even though designed to help him in a specific activity, complicates the situation. When he has solved most of the problems, he then becomes proficient in the use of the equipment. If we realize that some divers hang twelve or more pieces of gear on themselves, it becomes evident that it is desirable to become familiar with one item before adding another. Eventually the diver may become skilled in the use of all equipment available to him and knowledgeably select only that which is pertinent to planned activity.

CHOOSING THE FACE MASK

Face masks are designed to fulfill a specific need, to provide a constant layer of air between the eyes and a transparent lens. Since this basic piece of equipment must be adaptable to use with other equipment, mainly snorkel and scuba, the designed shape covers only the nose and eyes. Inclusion of the nose permits pressure equalization of contained air with that of ambient water.

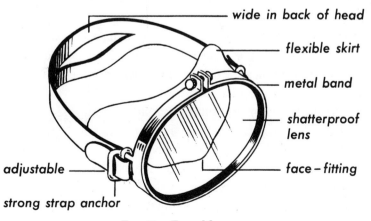

FIG. 13.   FACE MASK

The variations of design are multiple and purposeful. A variety of facial contours must be taken into account and accommodated. Individual needs or desires dictate size, volume, and lens design. Facilitation of associated functions are provided for by incorporation of "purge" valves and nose pinch devices. The majority are built for comfort, efficiency, and durability.

The final choice should be governed by size, shape, comfort, and positive seal. Size and shape are optional; comfort and positive seal are imperative. Essential features are a soft, flexible, face-fitting skirt, shatterproof or tempered glass lens secured by a metal band, an adjustable, head-fitting, well-anchored head strap. Nonessential but individually desirable are clearing (purge) valve and construction which permits pinching the nostrils shut.

Before you purchase a mask, place it over your eyes and nose *without donning the head strap.* Observe the skirt contour so as to avoid placing the mask on upside down. The skirt edge should contact your face completely. Inhale slightly with the mask in place. If desirable seal is obtained, the mask will remain in place until you exhale. Try several types, keeping in mind adaptability, comfort, and efficiency.

A good mask rates good care. Avoid contact with oil or grease (suntan lotions, hair dressing, and some cosmetics). Rinse or wash as necessary after use. Protect the lens from scratches or cracking. Check all parts and especially purge valves before and after diving.

Choosing the Snorkel

Though multiple designs are available, most are basically designed as "J"-shaped tubes of rubber, neoprene, plastic, or adaptable combinations. The length of the tube above mouth level is generally 12 to 14 inches. Greater length is superfluous; with it breathing comfort is noticeably decreased, dead air space is increased, and no advantage gained.

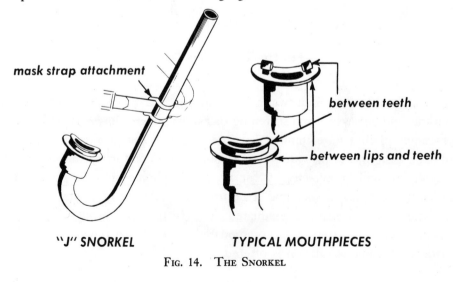

mask strap attachment

between teeth

between lips and teeth

"J" SNORKEL   TYPICAL MOUTHPIECES

Fig. 14. The Snorkel

Mask and snorkel combinations, mechanical gimmicks to keep water out, and designs alleged to permit several feet of submergence while breathing should be avoided. Most are clumsy and inefficient, and some are just plain dangerous.

Choose a design which is simple, light, adaptable to attachment on the face mask strap, and equipped with a soft, smooth, easily gripped mouthpiece. Most modern manufacturers of diving equipment provide these features, so the choice boils down to comfort and price. Purging valves located below the mouthpiece are a luxury rather than a necessity and add to the "things to be checked" list.

CHOOSING THE FINS

The evolution of this foot-area-increasing attachment from a board on the shoe to the many scientifically designed fins now available is an excellent example of the combined research and development necessary to make man

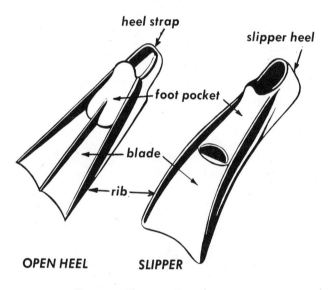

FIG. 15.   TYPICAL FIN DESIGNS

more adaptable to an underwater environment. Variations of total blade area, outline, and curvature, and stiffening of ribs to govern flexibility and increase efficiency of thrust are combined with a slipper or foot pocket and heel strap of such design as to provide positive control and comfort to the wearer. No one design will be satisfactory for all, so the choice must be governed by individual physical ability and structure. Some degree of limitation is built in. Since most are made in graduated sizes (to fit small through large feet— usually two shoe sizes are accommodated by each size) with proportional blade sizes, some regulation is offered.

Choosing the Weight Belt

An essential item of equipment for those who, because of positive buoyancy, have trouble submerging and remaining submerged, the weight belt should be sturdily constructed, flexible, and wide enough to be comfortable when worn next to the skin or over diving equipment. It must be equipped with a quick-release mechanism or double "D" rings for the safety hitch. These must permit positive release with one hand. Belt size (girth) adjustment methods are variable according to buckle design. Such adjustment is necessary, not only to fit the individual but to provide for additional length when protective clothing is worn and weights added. *Do not tie the belt material excess.* Better to let it dangle than to eliminate the effectiveness of the quick release.

Weights should be so constructed that they can be readily added to or removed from the selected belt. Bilateral distribution in equal amount is desirable for providing stability. Determination of required weight, as described in Chapter 6, "Skills of Skin and Scuba Diving," prior to purchase may provide some economy.

FIT THE WEIGHT BELT TO GO ON LAST AND COME OFF FIRST.

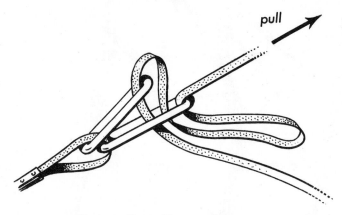

pull

FIG. 16   QUICK-RELEASE BUCKLE

Protective Clothing

The prime reason for wearing some type of insulating clothing is the prevention of body heat loss to the water. Choice of type of clothing and area to be covered will depend on intended use, individual need, and, in many instances, price. Such protective clothing may be divided into three categories: wet suits (foam rubber or neoprene), absorbent cloth, and dry suits (sheet rubber).

WET SUITS

These are designed to permit a small amount of water between the diver and suit. The fit should be snug enough to prevent a general flow-through of water but not so tight as to restrict movement or cause discomfort.

It is generally conceded that the foam material be covered with "skin" (smooth material, rubber, neoprene, or nylon) both inside and out. This smooth surface will facilitate donning and doffing, strengthen the material, and make general maintenance easier. The thickness of material governs the insulating properties. Suit material is offered in thicknesses ⅛, ³⁄₁₆, ¼, and ⅜ inch. The thicker materials afford more insulation but impose some problems due to bulk. Definite temperature assignment for each thickness would be misleading because of individual tolerance, length of time in the water, tailoring, and total area covered.

Barring extensive destruction of the suit, no drastic efficiency loss occurs when the material is torn during a dive. Repairs can be easily and quickly made, using liquid adhesives recommended by the manufacturer. (Further discussion of wet suits will be found in Chapter 6.)

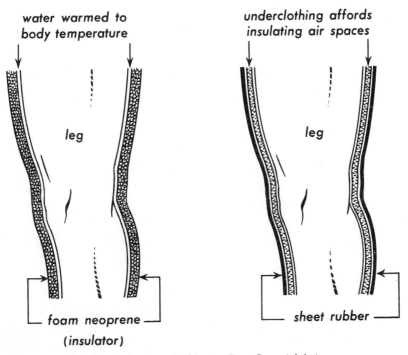

FIG. 17 WET SUIT (left) AND DRY SUIT (right)

ABSORBENT CLOTHING

Most any adaptable articles of clothing designed primarily to provide insulation against heat loss to air will afford some protection in water. Some thermal jackets and pants, though efficient when dry, will give little protection when wet. Generally, close-fitting garments of fibrous or wool-like material, closely woven or tight knit, will provide limited protection for short periods of time in water temperatures above 65° F. Substitution for specifically designed protective clothing is *not implied*. (Types and problems are discussed in Chapter 6.)

DRY SUITS

Fabrications of sheet rubber, which in itself has little insulating properties, are designed generally to provide head-to-toe leakproof covering. Several types are available: Front and back entry suits are one piece and molded seamless or cemented and stripped; entry is made through one large midsection opening which is then gathered, folded, and fastened by clamps or rings. Another design is two pieces, top and bottom; after donning both sections, the two are rolled together at the waist or sealed by use of a waist ring device. Wrist cuffs or rings and necessarily snug face openings are not conducive to comfort. Worn over adequate wool or thermal underwear and properly sealed, this type of protective suit will provide comfort for longer periods and permit diving in colder water than a heavy wet suit. Combination of dry suit over wet suit merges the advantages of both and permits diving at minimum temperatures.

Poor seal, trapped air, and possible rupture of material are discussed in Chapters 2 and 6. Regular maintenance should include thorough examination, testing for leaks, and careful storing (dried and powdered with talc). Oil, grease, volatile liquids (gasoline, kerosene, mineral spirits, etc.) and prolonged heat will alter the elastic properties of rubber and must be avoided.

The foregoing description of protective clothing has been of basic nature. Consultation with knowledgeable and experienced divers in your part of the world should provide enough information to guide your selection. Regardless of choice, it must be remembered that none are 100 per cent efficient and that the effects of continued heat loss can be dangerous.

THE FLOAT

The float, whether an inner tube, inflated raft, modified surfboard, or other satisfactory improvisation, should be striped or painted with bright color and equipped with a "Diver Down" flag. (The flag should be on a standard of sufficient length as to be easily visible.) Such precaution will make the anchored float easier to locate and will indicate the presence of divers to boat operators.

This float can be used as a surface base, a resting station, and, in an emergency, a rescue device. Suitable racks or holding devices can be rigged to

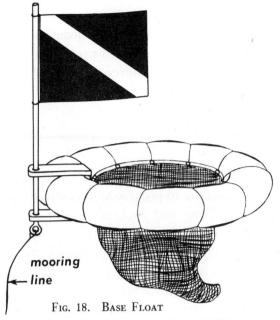

FIG. 18. BASE FLOAT

Inner Tube, Diver Down Flag, and Carryall Net

attach equipment and to provide "out of the water" storage for speared fish. If random coverage of a large area is anticipated and conditions permit, a tow line from the float to the diver will assure its proximity when desired.

PERSONAL FLOAT

A personal flotation device is considered essential by many civilian, professional, and military organizations even when the base float or surface craft

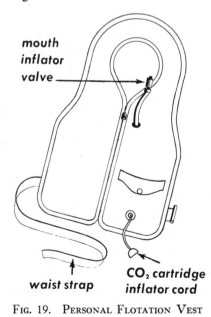

FIG. 19. PERSONAL FLOTATION VEST

base is provided. Many such devices are available, most of them inflated by CO_2 cartridges when needed. Although expensive, the *vest* type provides the most efficient support of the conscious or disabled diver. These provide readily available means of cartridge or breath inflation and, because of design, are safer to use.

DIVER DOWN FLAG

The diver's flag is an essential item for a diving expedition whenever boat traffic can be expected. Posters showing this red flag with the diagonal white strip have been put up in many boathouses across the country by diving clubs. Use your flag and advertise its significance; respect the flag of other divers. The screw of a large or small boat is too dangerous to take lightly. Navy and Coast Guard boats may fly a "Baker" flag (solid red) when they have a diver in the water or request that other craft keep away for other reasons.

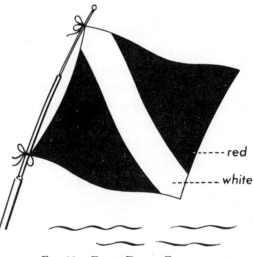

FIG. 20.   DIVER DOWN FLAG

Tools

In order to take such game as fish, shellfish or crustaceans, it is necessary to have specialized tools. They can be divided into spearing, prying, and cutting devices.

CHOOSING THE SPEAR

Here, an almost infinite variety can be made or purchased. The thrust-type spear, although not the most efficient, may be best for the beginner. Its use can be likened to hunting with a single-shot rifle as compared with a repeating rifle. Skill in stalking and accuracy in spearing are developed with the simpler equipment. Since spears must be sharp to be effective, they must be handled with care. Spear accidents are common, some serious. Points should be covered with cork or rubber when not being used in the water. These weapons must be stored carefully. In one case a boy leaped into the back of a car, where a carelessly placed spear injured him severely.

Handle the thrust-type spear with care at all times, but particularly when going through breaking surf. When ascending from a dive without a fish, avoid pointing tines upward. Surface swimmers have been speared by careless divers. Always look up when surfacing. Avoid thrusting spear points against rocks. When you are swimming through kelp, the spear can be trailed to avoid tangling.

CHOOSING THE SPEAR GUN

Of many designs, most are trigger activated. The shaft is propelled by springs, rubber, or compressed gas. Choose one with a dependable safety device. Avoid overpowered guns, since they are frequently difficult to cock in the water and, unless you know you are going for big game, the added expense and power are wasted. Detonating spear heads are for big game hunters only.

TREAT ALL SPEAR GUNS LIKE HIGH-POWERED RIFLES! Do not go through breaking surf with gun cocked. In fact, it should be cocked only after the diver has arrived at the fishing area and is in the water. The "safety" should be engaged until just before firing. Keep gas-powered guns out of the sun's heat. They have been known to fire because of heat-expanded gas. In one case, even though the shaft was disengaged, a serious eye injury resulted from the gas blast. When looking for fish from the surface, be alert to the direction in which the gun is pointing. It is easy, when using a snorkel, with the face in the water, to point the spear accidentally at another swimmer.

Be sure of your target before firing. A spear shaft can be a deadly weapon. Do not fire spears on the beach when others may be endangered. Spear practice on the beach has jeopardized friendly relationships between the beach-going public and the diving fraternity. Store all gear on the beach in a neat and safe manner. Always detach spear points. Aboard boats a special box or locker should be provided to contain spears and keep them out of the way. Spears must not be tied to the diver. They can be secured to the float. In one case a diver was apparently towed to his death by a huge fish he had speared.

CHOOSING THE PRYING TOOL

Almost any strong iron, steel, or aluminum bar can be used. A strong screwdriver is a satisfactory improvisation. The tool should be from 8 to 12 inches in length and slightly curved. It should be chisel-edged at one end, but the edge should NOT be sharp. As is required in some states, measurements can be filed onto the "iron," to measure shellfish. If fastened to the wrist, the lanyard should be flexible. Do NOT use strong cord. Strips of rubber are satisfactory and are easily replaced.

Choosing the Knife

A knife is a useful tool for cutting lines, kelp, or other objects while diving, or for cleaning and preparing game on the beach. The knife should be considered a tool, not a weapon. The blade should be short, with one sharp edge and one saw edge. It need not have a sharp point. Do not use dagger-type devices. This tool should be carried in a dependable sheath at all times and secured in such a way that the handle is close to the body and easily reached. A floating handle may prevent loss.

Open-Circuit Scuba

Essentially all open-circuit scuba are the same. They utilize a high-pressure air cylinder, a cylinder valve assembly, harness, a valve for controlling the flow of high-pressure air, the necessary breathing tubes, and a mask or mouthpiece to permit inhalation and an exhalation valve.

The valve for controlling the high-pressure air may be a needle valve (as is used in a constant-flow unit) or an automatic demand regulator.

For most sport diving the scuba should also feature a reserve air or warning device to indicate to the diver that he is running out of air.

Open-Circuit Continuous-Flow Equipment

Open-circuit continuous-flow systems are generally considered impractical for diving because of the waste of air and the resultant short diving time.

All straight-flow units have a potential hazard in that the high-pressure air is fed directly to the diver. Any excess air is allowed to escape from an exhaust valve that normally is an integral part of the mouthpiece. Such a unit, which does not have an ample exhaust valve, would be extremely hazardous.

Open-Circuit Demand-Type Scuba

The flow of air from the high-pressure cylinder to the diver is controlled by an automatic pressure-reducing demand regulator in a demand-type scuba. Regulators may have either one or two stages of pressure reduction.

Regulator Air Flow Requirements*

There is a great deal of misunderstanding and misinformation regarding the meaning of easy breathing in a regulator. Few people actually understand

---

* This section and accompanying drawings (Figures 21–26) used by permission of the U.S. Divers Company. Reference to U.S. Divers equipment is an excerpt from a brochure put out by that company and is neither an advocation of deep dives nor necessarily an equipment endorsement.

what is necessary to give a diver the large volumes of air flow needed when working underwater. As a result, many divers are selecting their regulators on the basis of a "pretty case" or a "nice-looking mouthpiece." Others attempt to judge regulator performance and "easy breathing" by the slight effort necessary to depress the regulator diaphragm and start an air flow. Such effort has very little to do with actual performance.

As an illustration, put a straw in a person's mouth while he is sitting quietly and he will have no difficulty breathing through the straw. This is "easy breathing." But let that person try running while breathing through the same straw and you have an example of requirements in regulator performance.

In a regulator, we are concerned with great volumes of air flow with NO INCREASE IN SUCTION EFFORT. The extremely large volumes of air flow demanded from a regulator are illustrated in Figure 21.

Increase in Air Flows

The figure of 1 cubic foot per minute normal consumption is not accurate as air consumption varies between individuals. But 1 cubic foot per minute is close enough to illustrate the tremendous increase in volume of flow required during exertion. The estimate of three times normal consumption during exertion is conservative. But it is obvious that a tremendous volume of flow is required below 50 feet. At 100 feet, a diver under working conditions

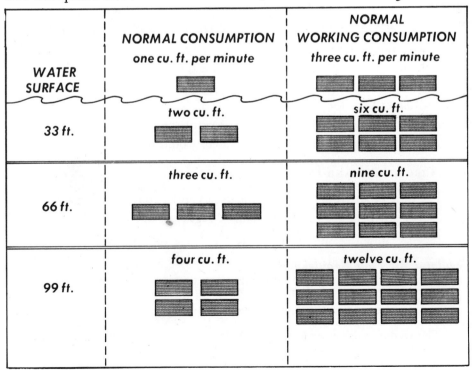

FIG. 21. REGULATOR AIR FLOW REQUIREMENTS

consumes 12 cubic feet per minute. This is a tremendous air flow. Any restriction to breathing in a regulator will give the same effect as trying to run around the block while breathing through a straw. The large air flows must be obtained with NO INCREASE IN SUCTION EFFORT.

Actually our lungs do not occupy a greater volume under pressure. The molecules are pressed closer together, air becomes thick, and forcing it through an opening is somewhat the same as the flow of syrup through a straw as compared to the flow of water through a straw. Another comparison is the flow of light traffic through a subway door as compared to the congestion of traffic during the rush hour. The size of the opening determines the number of people who can travel easily through a doorway and it also determines the amount of dense air which can flow easily through an orifice.

The result of such restriction to breathing has been experienced by every "old time" diver who has attempted to work underwater at any appreciable depth. With insufficient volume of air flow he becomes starved for air. His suction effort increases tremendously in an attempt to increase the flow. This increased effort accelerates his exhaustion and causes a demand for ever greater volumes of air flow. At this point even stopping to rest while still under pressure will not ease the demand for great volumes of flow and the diver is gasping for breath until he returns to more shallow water or the surface.

This example is an extreme, but degrees of this exhaustion from restricted breathing are experienced every day by divers working in moderately deep water with inadequate regulators. This exertion in breathing also uses air at a faster rate and cylinders are more quickly exhausted.

Now let's look at regulator designs and see why breathing is restricted in some types and not in others.

The Upstream and Downstream Single Stage

An engineer designing a regulator mechanism is immediately faced with the problem of variation of pressure from 2,000 psi to 200 psi in the cylinder. This cylinder pressure acts on the valve seat to either open or close the valve depending upon whether the valve opens "downstream" or "upstream" with the flow of air. Both types are illustrated in Figure 22.

In the "downstream" type it is clear that high-pressure air entering through the orifice tends to OPEN THE VALVE. The force exerted is calculated by multiplying the area of the orifice times the pressure in the cylinder. For example:

Tank Pressure		Orifice		Opening Force
2,000 psi	×	.01	=	20 psi
500 psi	×	.01	=	5 psi

This opening force of high-pressure air vitally affects the operation of, the regulator. A mechanical force, such as a spring, must be balanced against the force of the cylinder air pressure.

It is also clear that the opening force will vary with the pressure in the cylinder. A full cylinder of 2,000 pounds pressure will exert more opening force than when its pressure has dropped to 500 pounds. The spring, or mechanical force, calculated to hold the valve closed against a full cylinder pressure, makes the valve more difficult to open at a low cylinder pressure.

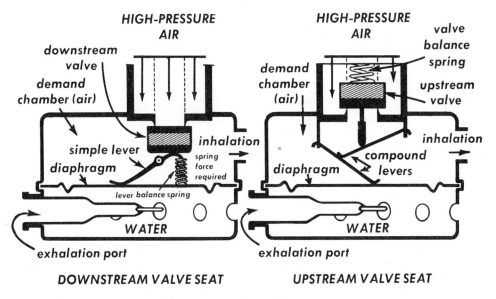

FIG. 22.   ONE-STAGE REGULATOR

In the "upstream" type of valve the variation is exactly the opposite. The high-pressure cylinder air acts as a CLOSING FORCE and tends to seat the valve. As cylinder pressure drops, this force becomes less, and breathing becomes easier. This is at low cylinder pressure—at the end of a dive.

The diameter of the orifice is extremely important in regulator design. Too great a variation in breathing between high and low pressures cannot be tolerated. In the two-hose type of regulator, large orifices and a degree of variation can be tolerated because of the extremely large diaphragm and the space available inside the case for a mechanical leverage advantage. Since the great area of the diaphragm makes it extremely sensitive to slight differences in pressure, a variation in effort required in opening the valve is not noticed. Because of the size of the diaphragm, large orifices can be used and no restriction to breathing is encountered.

But diving engineers, not satisfied with the single-stage solution, developed a regulator which gave less variation and permitted larger flows. The result is the two-stage, two-hose regulator.

Two-Stage, Two-Hose Type

In this type, high-pressure cylinder air is reduced to breathing pressure in two stages. The first-stage valve reduces cylinder pressures to a lower predetermined pressure in the intermediate chamber leading to the second-stage valve. The large diaphragm activating the second-stage valve is then balanced against a much lower and more consistent intermediate pressure.

In the first stage, high-pressure cylinder air acts as a closing force tending to push the valve through the orifice. Counteracting the closing force of the cylinder air is a large spring pressing against a small diaphragm with a stem attached to the valve. Movement of the diaphragm up or down moves the stem up and down and opens or closes the valve.

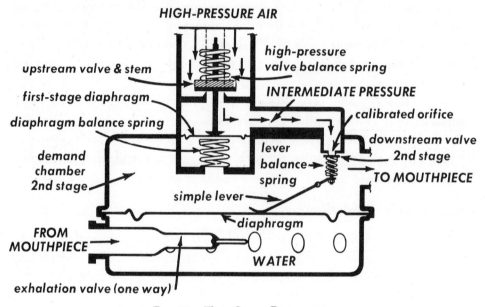

FIG. 23.   TWO-STAGE REGULATOR

The heavy spring is manually adjusted to hold the valve open against the closing force of a full cylinder of air until the intermediate pressure increases sufficiently to compress the spring and close the valve. When intermediate pressure reaches a predetermined point, usually around 100 psi over ambient pressure, the diaphragm is depressed and the valve closes.

In the second stage, a slight inhalation causes the large diaphragm to move. This opens the second-stage valve and allows air to flow to the mouthpiece. In this case, the large diaphragm controls only the low, intermediate pressure leading to the second-stage valve.

But once again we have a variation in pressure in the intermediate chamber due to variation in cylinder pressure.

The heavy spring against the first-stage diaphragm is adjusted against a full cylinder to give a calculated intermediate pressure. When cylinder pressure falls, the force of high-pressure air seating the valve also falls. Then the spring holds the valve open longer and the intermediate pressure increases to a point above the predetermined pressure. The intermediate pressure must increase sufficiently to depress the diaphragm and the spring until the first stage valve again closes.

Once again the diameter of the orifice in the first stage determines the degree of pressure variation in the intermediate chamber. The large-diameter diaphragm in a two-hose regulator permits a degree of variation from large orifices. Thus adequate volumes of air flow are obtained with no increase in suction effort.

The first stage is depth-compensated, as air pressure in the housing is always equal to the surrounding water pressure. As this pressure increases with depth, it adds to the pressure of the spring against the small diaphragm and opens the first-stage valve. The valve stays open until intermediate pressure equals the surrounding water pressure plus the predetermined pressure at the surface.

The "downstream" type of valve in the second stage opens more easily with an increase in intermediate pressure. Since intermediate pressure increases as tank pressure falls, a two-stage, two-hose regulator of this design will breathe easiest when cylinder pressure is low—at the end of a dive when fatigue is a factor.

Ordinary Single-Hose First Stage

The standard first-stage valve used with single-hose regulators works very much the same as the first stage in two-hose regulators. The hose leading to the second stage at the mouthpiece carries the intermediate pressure.

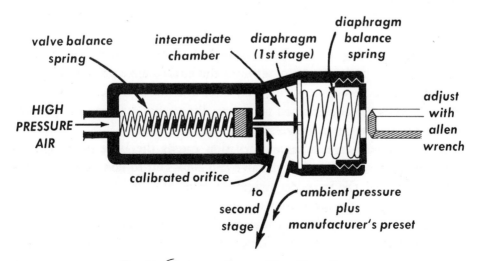

FIG. 24. STANDARD SINGLE-HOSE FIRST STAGE

Here again, high-pressure cylinder air acts as a closing force seating the first-stage valve.

The spring pushing against the diaphragm counteracts this force and must be adjusted to open the valve against the maximum pressure from a full cylinder. When intermediate pressure increases to a predetermined pressure, the valve closes.

When the cylinder is opened, air flows through the orifice into the intermediate chamber and into the hose leading to the second stage. When this intermediate pressure reaches approximately 100 pounds, or other predetermined figure, it pushes against the diaphragm, compresses the spring, and the valve closes.

The single-hose first stage is depth compensated by water pressure which enters the spring area, presses the diaphragm upward, and opens the valve. The valve will remain open until air in the intermediate chamber is equal to surrounding water pressure plus the calculated predetermined pressure.

But again, we have variation due to changing cylinder pressures. A low cylinder pressure exerts less closing force on the valve. The spring will hold the valve open until intermediate pressure in the hose increases sufficiently to depress the diaphragm and close the valve. In some regulators the increase in hose pressure is as great as 50 per cent.

In single-hose regulators the diaphragms are much smaller than in two hose regulators and are extremely sensitive to variations in pressure. The number of square inches of surface area in single-hose diaphragms is so small that slight variations in hose pressure make a great difference in breathing effort.

In order to reduce the amount of variation it is necessary to reduce the size of the orifice in the first stage. Remember the closing force seating the first-stage valve is the area of the orifice times the cylinder pressure plus the spring pressure. Using a smaller orifice reduces the effect of cylinder pressure in closing the valve.

However, a small orifice adds resistance to breathing when large volumes of air flow are required. It is similar to breathing through a straw.

Balanced First Stage

In the balanced first-stage valve, cylinder air pressure has no effect in seating the valve. Remember that in an ordinary first-stage valve the closing force *normally* exerted by cylinder air is calculated by multiplying the area of the orifice times the cylinder pressure.

Closing the orifice in a standard first-stage valve would neutralize the effect of this air pressure in seating the valve. The same effect as closing the orifice is achieved in the balanced valve.

The small drawing in Figure 25 showing a stick inside a can illustrates

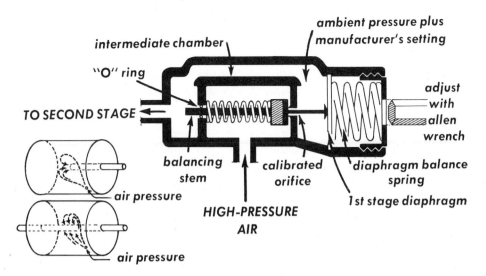

FIG. 25. BALANCED FIRST STAGE

what has been accomplished. The can with the end of the stick inside illustrates an unbalanced valve. Pressure applied to the can tends to drive the stick outside. The diameter of the stick determines the force with which it will be expelled.

The can that has the stick completely through it illustrates a balanced valve. Pressure inside the can has no effect on the stick as it is neutralized in all directions. The diameter of the stick makes no difference.

In a balanced valve, a valve stem of exactly the same diameter as the orifice is extended *outside* the chamber. High pressure is not exerted on the end of the valve stem, and we have the same result as the stick extended completely through the can.

With cylinder air pressure neutralized, only the mechanical forces of springs affect operation of the valve. These springs can be set to give exactly the desired intermediate pressure. And this pressure will remain the same over all stages of cylinder pressure.

What is more important to a scuba diver, with the valve unaffected by variations in cylinder pressure, large orifice diameters can be used to give LARGE VOLUMES OF AIR FLOW WITH NO INCREASE IN SUCTION EFFORT. The resistance to breathing caused by straining air through a tiny opening has been eliminated.

The balanced valve is also depth compensated. The pressure in the intermediate chamber and air hose is always equal to the pressure of the surrounding water *plus* the factory setting. To protect the valve stem and "O" ring from contamination due to contact with salt water, sand, and dirt, a special housing has been developed to contain the valve stem *inside* the housing and still maintain depth compensation.

The tremendous volume of air flow with only a slight suction effort obtained from a balanced valve is the reason Hannes Keller selected a Calypso regulator for his world record dive to 820 feet.

Now let's look at the second stages commonly used in conjunction with an ordinary first stage and with the Calypso balanced valve.

Single-Hose Second Stages

Most widely used in the second stage of single-hose regulators is the *tilt valve* outlined in Figure 26. The cases containing the valve mechanism are of all sizes and shapes but their operation is essentially the same.

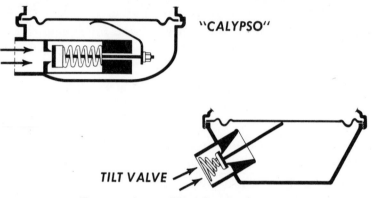

FIG. 26.   SINGLE-HOSE SECOND STAGES

The other second-stage mechanism outlined in Figure 26 is that of the *Calypso*.

It is obvious from the drawing that a Calypso second stage is far more expensive to manufacture than the simple, inexpensive tilt valve. There are definite, positive advantages in the Calypso mechanism which more than justify the extra expense.

The most important feature is in the *upstream* or *downstream* opening of the valves. A tilt valve opens *upstream*, against the pressure of air in the hose. Any variation which produces an overpressure in the hose will tend to drive the valve seat against the orifice and increase resistance to breathing. The variation of ordinary first stages produces an overpressure in the hose at low cylinder pressure and a tilt valve used with these gives the greatest resistance to breathing when cylinder pressure is low—at the end of a dive.

The Calypso-type second-stage valve opens downstream with the flow of air. An overpressure in the hose tends to make the valve easier to open. Thus, with the variation of a standard first-stage valve, this type of second stage will breathe easier when cylinder pressure is low—at the end of a dive.

Equally, or even more important, the upstream opening of a tilt valve requires a safety valve to release hose pressure in case of a first-stage valve leak. High-pressure cylinder air leaking into the hose cannot escape. Pressure forces the tilt valve against the seat. Without a safety valve to release over-pressure, the hose would burst.

Safety valves cannot always be depended upon. A regulator may be in use more than a year without occasion to use or test the safety valve operation. It is exposed to salt water, sunshine, sand, etc., and when needed, the relief valve may be stuck. In such an event, the tilt valve will be jammed against the seat and fail to operate or the hose may rupture.

In the Calypso-type downstream valve an overpressure in the hose simply forces the valve open and extra pressure bleeds harmlessly out through the exhaust. This is your safety valve, and it is tested each time you breathe. The downstream valve is a foolproof "failsafe" operation. Also, a tilt valve must tilt at an angle of 30 degrees to the orifice before a full flow of air equal to the area of the orifice can be obtained. This requires a large deflection of the diaphragm to get maximum flow.

In a "straight-away" opening valve, such as the Calypso, the seat must move only one fourth of the diameter of the orifice to obtain a full flow. Thus, only a slight movement of the lever is required to obtain full flow of air.

The Calypso second stage combined with the balanced valve first stage is the ideal combination used by Hannes Keller in his world record dives. At these depths a regulator which gives adequate flows will obviously give the greatest flow with the least resistance at ordinary depths. To a diver, this means less fatigue and more underwater time from each cylinder of air.

Single-Stage Demand Regulator

A single-stage demand regulator is one in which there is only one valve mechanism between the cylinders and the mount. It can be made with fewer parts and may therefore be less expensive than a two-stage unit. This is one of the primary advantages, provided the design features of the regulator take into consideration the inherent characteristics of a single-stage regulator.

All demand regulators must provide a more or less constant volume of air from the cylinder regardless of the pressure within the cylinder. Orifices within the regulator have a fixed diameter and can therefore deliver only a fixed amount of air at any given pressure. The amount of air that can pass through an orifice of a given diameter varies with the cylinder pressure and with depth. If the orifice in a single-stage regulator is not large enough to pass adequate amounts of air at all cylinder pressures and depths, breathing may be considerably restricted. This tendency has been overcome in most single-stage regulators by systems of compound levers, larger orifices, and other means. As a result of engineering skills, today's single-stage regulators may be considered equal to most two-stage regulators and superior to some, provided other factors (such as quality of material and construction) are equal.

Two-Stage Demand Regulator

Demand-type regulators having two stages of pressure reduction are available with both stages of pressure reduction in one regulator and with separate regulators for the two stages of pressure reduction.

Generally when two housings are used for the two stages of pressure reduction the second stage is mounted on the diving mask or mouthpiece and connected to the first-stage regulator on the air bottle by a suitable length of pressure tubing.

The original model of the Aqua-Lung is an example of a two-stage regulator with both stages of pressure reduction in one case. The first stage reduces the cylinder pressure to about 100 psi above the ambient pressure, the second stage to that of the surrounding water pressure.

Function of Regulators

All regulators are essentially air valves that are operated by the motion of a diaphragm against a lever system to open the valve. The arrangement of the levers and other components may vary, but the basic principle remains the same.

When a regulator is not connected to an air supply the regular components are in a state of mechanical balance determined by the design of the unit and achieved in its assembly.

When a single-stage regulator is attached to an air supply the air flows only to the high-pressure valve seat, which is closed by the action of a valve spring and of the air pressure. On inhalation from the regulator the diaphragm is depressed by the surrounding water pressure. This force, amplified by a lever system, opens the valve allowing air to flow to the diver.

In the case of a two-stage regulator attached to an air supply, air flows into the high-pressure valve, forcing the high-pressure diaphragm to compress the high-pressure spring. The action of this spring is transmitted back to the high-pressure valve by a pin which holds the high-pressure valve open against the action of the high-pressure valve spring. When the pressure against the high-pressure diaphragm reaches a predetermined value, the high-pressure spring will have compressed sufficiently to allow the high-pressure valve to close, shutting off the air supply. This air is held in the regulator by the low-pressure valve which is actuated only by the diaphragm when the diver inhales.

BREATHING HOSES

The breathing hoses used with scuba must be large enough to supply the volume of air required for a diver who may have to work very hard. They must have flexibility to permit movement of his head in all directions, and they must be so designed and constructed that they will not kink. The corrugated tubing presently used meets these requirements.

NON-RETURN, OR CHECK-VALVE, SYSTEM

A check-valve mouthpiece has been designed to prevent water from entering the inhalation tube of the breathing hoses. Also the check valves keep any water that may enter the exhalation tube from returning to the mouthpiece and make clearing a flooded circuit much easier.

AIR RESERVE VALVE

Scuba should be equipped with an air reserve device or valve for safety. Several such devices are available.

One method is referred to as the "constant" preset air reserve valve. In this method a spring-loaded valve is closed against the air in the cylinder at a predetermined pressure, generally about 300 psi. When the cylinder pressure reaches the predetermined point, slight difficulty in breathing will be noticed. Pulling a lever releases the remainder of the air and restores normal breathing at least long enough to permit surfacing. It should be remembered that the pressure at which warning occurs is internal cylinder pressure and not pressure above the surrounding water pressure. Therefore, when diving at a depth of 100 feet (a pressure of approximately 50 psi) a 300-pound reserve would be only 250 psi above the water pressure. This factor must be considered when planning the dive. Another factor even more important is that an air reserve on one cylinder of a two- or three-tank unit contains the reserve air in only one cylinder. The other cylinders will be nearly empty before the need is felt for releasing the reserve air. When reserve air is released it will equalize into the two or three cylinders at one half or one third the pressure held in reserve by the reserve valve. In comparatively deep diving this may provide only a few pounds of pressure in the cylinders in excess of the surrounding water pressure.

There are others, such as limiting orifices, noisemakers, and the like, with varying degrees of effectiveness.

The usual practice for double and triple tank blocks is to set the air reserve spring at 500 and 750 psi respectively.

OVERPRESSURE BREATHING DEVICE

Demand regulators release air as a result of a reduction of pressure in the air chamber created by the diver's inhalation. The effort required to activate the demand-valve depends not only upon the "stiffness" of the demand system, but also upon the difference in water pressure existing between the lungs and the diaphragm of the regulator. Normally this amounts to only 6 or 7 inches or about one-quarter pound of pressure per square inch. However, this muscular exertion must be maintained as long as air is required and may create a considerable strain on the chest muscles.

A development known as "overpressure breathing" eliminates part of this required effort except at the very beginning of inhalation.

The "overpressure breathing" device is a venturi tube system designed so that the air from the regulator, rushing through the venturi tube, creates a slight reduction in pressure in the air chamber, much as occurs on inhalation. This allows the water pressure to continue to hold the diaphragm in an open position giving an increased flow of air with less effort.

An overpressure breathing system may be used to advantage, particularly at great depths, where the resistance to breathing increases because of increased air density. However, such a system may reduce the duration of the air supply considerably. The possibility of such reduction should be taken into account when planning dives involving depths beyond average.

Scuba Harness

All scuba harnesses should be equipped with quick-release buckles to permit rapid removal of the equipment, if ditching becomes necessary.

Most manufacturers have designed a special harness for their own particular type of unit. Generally the recommended harness will prove superior to one of another design. However, some features of another harness may be used to advantage for a particular type of diving work.

The most recent trend is toward the plastic, form-fitting back pack. Tank attachment devices are simple and adjustable as desired. Harness is uncomplicated, adjustable, and equipped with quick-release fastenings. These features provide for convenient adjustment or disassembly when desired, usually without special tools. Cost will be one of the factors affecting selection but whatever the choice may be, it must feature necessary quick-release fastenings of all harness. Complete knowledge of design and function peculiarities prior to any diving is a necessity.

Advantages of Scuba

Scuba enjoys several advantages over conventional helmet diving equipment for sport diving use. Low initial cost, less operational cost, and more nearly complete mobility, are probably the three most important considerations.

Cost

For the sport diver who expects no returns from his diving equipment except enjoyment, the initial cost is quite important. A complete scuba diving outfit may cost about $250, but a comparably complete helmet diving outfit would cost approximately $1,500.

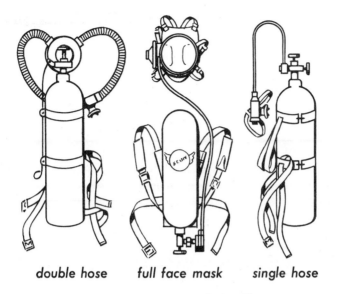

double hose   full face mask   single hose

FIG. 27. OPEN-CIRCUIT SCUBA TYPES

Operational cost of scuba is also less. A helmet diver must hire helpers at considerable expense. Also, his base of operation and mode of transportation must be considerably larger and more expensive than that of a scuba diver. Cost of air, per hour of diving, is about the same for both scuba and helmet diving. However, maintenance, insurance, and other incidental costs are considerably less for scuba.

MOBILITY

Normally, mobility is the scuba diver's greatest asset. With no air hoses leading to the surface, the scuba diver can submerge, swim to another location, and surface at still another. A scuba diver can maintain neutral buoyancy, swim in any direction, and ascend and descend with greater ease than can a helmet diver.

Disadvantages of Scuba

Scuba does, in spite of an apparent superiority over helmet equipment, have some distinct disadvantages. The relatively short duration of the air supply, is definitely a limiting factor. As presently used, depth is also a limiting factor. *Dives beyond a depth of 130 feet are impractical for sport diving because of the limited air supply and the need for decompression.* Further limitation is imposed by certain types of equipment. Also, one of the greatest advantages of the scuba diver, almost complete mobility, may become a disadvantage under certain conditions of current, visibility, and work requirements.

Complete lack of communication with the surface and only limited communication between divers is also a problem.

Disadvantages of scuba may, under certain conditions, become actually hazardous and should be considered carefully when planning a dive.

Greater protection from environmental hazards exist when using helmet equipment. This is particularly true when working around sharp objects, such as coral, barnacles, and rocks.

Reliability of the air supply is another consideration. A scuba diver is subjected to all the hazards of a helmet diver, but he carries air for only an hour or two of survival in the water. Exhaustion or loss of air may create a hazardous situation.

Choosing Scuba

As previously mentioned, a check of equipment catalogues leaves the new diver confused and at a loss as to which regulator is best. The choice may be narrowed by considering average use, adaptability to need and ease of maintenance. Cost is not a major factor, since there is little difference between double-hose and single-hose types of comparative quality.

If general use will be confined to sport diving in shallow or moderate depths, with no extended activity planned or foreseen, the less expensive single-stage double-hose type, of approved design and manufacture, or the less expensive single-hose two-stage unit should be adequate. Modern equipment, even the least expensive, is generally tested for continual satisfactory function at depths far below the recommended sport diving limits.

Reserve valves, either tank valve or regulator attached type, are desirable if not mandatory for sport divers in the above instance.

If deeper, extended working dives are contemplated, it naturally follows that the best and most adaptable scuba outfit should be selected.

One does not expect the same overall performance from both jalopy and high-priced auto, though both may yield adequate performance under average conditions. Similar (though not the same) comparison may be made when choosing scuba. Modern technology, manufacture, and competition have removed the scuba "jalopy" from the scene, but we still have the equivalents of the standard and deluxe models.

Care of Open-Circuit Scuba

Most scuba are well made of materials intended for use in water. However, if the unit is to keep functioning, considerable care must be taken of the equipment. This care should begin the day of purchase.

Scuba Check Prior to Use

A thorough check and test of all equipment should be standard procedure when the equipment is purchased and prior to any dive. The use of a checklist may be warranted under certain conditions of sport diving involving a number of participants. The list should cover essential points of each piece of equipment. Particularly important, however, is a thorough check of the scuba itself.

Perhaps the most important is testing or checking the scuba cylinder pressure. A slow, almost undetectable leak may be present from a faulty fitting or from the valve's having been opened slightly during transportation. After the pressure has been determined, even though there may have been some loss of air, a safe dive can be planned.

Next, check the hoses, mouthpiece, mask, or other parts of the assembly for cracks, punctures, or other indications of weakness. Check to see that the harness is adjusted properly and free from signs of excessive wear, and that it is equipped with quick-release-type buckles.

After attaching the regulator to the cylinder, open the cylinder valve and check to see that there are no leaks from around the high-pressure block of the regulator. This may be determined by listening for the sound of escaping air. If there is any doubt about there being a leak, submerge the regulator and top of the cylinder in the water and visually check for leaking air, indicated by the presence of bubbles.

Also, check for air leaking through the regulator. Sometimes the regulator may get dirty, or a part may become worn, allowing for a constant flow of air. This not only wastes the air supply but may indicate serious mechanical trouble in the regulator that could become hazardous.

Inhale and exhale through the regulator before you enter the water to determine whether or not the unit is functioning properly.

When attaching the regulator to the cylinder valve, use caution to prevent damage to the high-pressure valve seat or "O" ring. If these parts become damaged, air will probably leak, causing a waste of air and allowing a dive of considerably shorter duration.

Again check the proper operation of the scuba when just below the surface of the water by inhaling and exhaling through the regulator and hoses.

Preventive Care After Use

All parts of the scuba should be thoroughly washed in clean, fresh water after use. This applies after use in either salt water or fresh water because saliva that may find its way into the breathing apparatus is as corrosive as salt water. Also, there is the possibility that the fresh water in which the dive was made contained silt or other foreign matter that should be rinsed from the unit before storing.

Most modern regulators are equipped with an attached "dust cap." The cap (plastic cone), attached to the yoke by a metal ring, should be inserted over the high-pressure seat and maintained by the thumb screw whenever the regulator is not attached to the tank valve. The cap serves to prevent entrance of dirt or water into the regulator through the high-pressure chamber.

Particular care should be taken to cleanse, exhaust, and check valves of all particles of dirt or grit. Even a small particle in one of these valves will hold it open, allowing water to enter the breathing system.

The rubber parts of the unit, such as breathing tubes and mouthpiece, should be washed, dried, and sprinkled with soapstone (crude talc) to help preserve the rubber. Any indication of cracking of the rubber parts, or stiffness, would be reason for replacement of rubber parts.

When tightening fittings, use a wrench of the correct size and design to prevent damage to the threads or sides of the nuts that may cause serious weakness.

A pipe wrench should never be used on the neck of a scuba cylinder, for it can cause nicks in the metal wall that will weaken the cylinder's strength by as much as 50 per cent or more. There have been several instances where cylinders have failed to pass recertification tests because of damage to the neck of the cylinder.

No work should ever be done on a cylinder, valve, or high-pressure fitting of any kind when the cylinder or fitting contains a gas under pressure.

REPAIR PROCEDURES

Unless you are qualified to work on high-pressure regulators and fittings, maintenance and repair of scuba should be limited to that required to prevent corrosion or other damage. The exception may be any necessary replacement of breathing hoses, mouthpieces, or exhaust valves. Avoid leaving the regulator in direct sunlight, as the ultraviolet rays may cause the hoses to deteriorate quite rapidly.

Current Interstate Commerce Commission regulations require that cylinders designed for containing high-pressure gases be tested and recertified every five years. When this ICC requirement was established it was not intended that the tested cylinder be used carelessly or under the adverse conditions present in scuba diving.

A safer policy would be to have the cylinders tested every year, or more often if visual inspection reveals any evidence of damage or deterioration, particularly after any unusual abuse, such as dropping, that might cause a deep scratch or other weakening of the metal, visible or otherwise.

COMPRESSED AIR CYLINDERS

The potential energy, and hazard, of a fully charged cylinder is very great, and the cylinders require special precautions in handling and storing.

In one accident involving a high-pressure cylinder, the valve was accidentally broken from the cylinder. The force of the escaping air (2,000 psi) jetted the cylinder through the roof of the shop and through the air for a distance of about two blocks. It struck a lawn and dug a strench six feet long and then richocheted into the side of a house with sufficient force to penetrate several inches. The blast of escaping air tore the clothes off the man who was working on the cylinder and might have caused serious injury.

When transporting cylinders, whether by automobile, boat, or other means, be sure all cylinders are securely tied, blocked, or held in place to prevent damage. An equal amount of care should be taken to see that no heavy object can fall on the unit and cause damage to the cylinders or fittings.

When storing cylinders in a car for transportation, place them so that the valve is toward the back of the car. The bottom of the cylinders should be blocked or resting against the front wall of the trunk. Cylinders should be prone and properly blocked to prevent side motion.

Considerable care should be taken to prevent accidentally striking the cylinders against a sharp object that could cause nicks or scratches. Otherwise these might produce a weak spot which would be a potential place of cleavage or explosion.

High-pressure air cylinders must be filled slowly, preferably while submerged in cold water to prevent a radical buildup of heat and pressure. They should never be filled beyond their rated working pressures.

All filling tubes, hoses, and fittings must be of high-pressure construction. Work should not be done on any cylinder, valve, or fitting while it is under pressure.

Cylinder harnesses should be in good condition. Inspect them frequently to see that all rivets and sewed fastenings are secure. Fasten all straps so that they can be released quickly.

Never use oil or grease on any high-pressure fittings. Use only Dow-Corning Silicon lubricating fluid for any fitting requiring lubrication, and then use sparingly.

Closed-Circuit Scuba

A history of diving shows that one of the first successful scubas was a closed-circuit, oxygen-rebreathing apparatus. However, the use of closed-circuit equipment has remained primarily military, with a few commercial applications. This is due to the more technical nature of the equipment, certain inherent hazards, and the requirement for a considerable amount of training if the equipment is to be used safely.

Semiclosed-Circuit Scuba

As the name implies, a semiclosed system permits partial rebreathing of the gas. This provides duration of a gas supply longer than can be achieved with open-circuit gear. A semiclosed system uses a mixed gas supply and has all the components of a closed-circuit system. In addition, two other features must be present. These are the reliable automatic-injector system and a special exhaust-valve system. Generally, a semiclosed system uses continuous injection of breathing gas and continuous exhaust.

USE OF CLOSED- AND SEMICLOSED-CIRCUIT SYSTEMS

Closed- and semiclosed-circuit scuba are considered unsafe for use by the average sport diver. The safe use of such equipment requires extensive knowledge and training acquired under close supervision. Disadvantages are imposed by depth limitation, gas supply control and continuous maintenance problems. Semiclosed units involving purchase or manufacture of mixed gases in specific proportion present too complex a problem to be considered for sport diving.

The dangers of anoxia due to insufficient oxygen content or lowered partial pressures, or oxygen poisoning due to high percentage content plus partial pressure increase during descent are ever present. Errors in depth calculation or incorrect valving might bring about either condition. Carbon dioxide accumulation due to failure of absorbent material or incorrect valving is another likely situation.

Whether due to design or human failure, the dangers inherent in the use of these types of scuba are not offset by low purchase price or "do it yourself" economy.

Helmet Diving Apparatus

Helmet diving apparatus involves equipment and techniques that require training by and supervision of a qualified instructor. The equipment is not generally considered suitable for sport diving, but will be discussed briefly for comparative purposes.

Helmet equipment (hard hat) may include open or closed helmets. The closed helmet, traditional gear of the so-called deep sea diver, is attached directly to the suit. Additional parts of the dress are heavy-weight belt, weighted shoes, necessary valves, fittings, air hose, intercommunication system wires, and a lifeline firmly attached so as to insure recovery of the diver in the event of accident.

All the hoses, wires, and lines act as a heavy, cumbersome umbilical cord from diver to base vessel. The diver is dependent on his base crew for air supply, timing, ascent, and hose payout—in short, this type of diving is work, not sport.

Open or shallow-water helmet equipment utilizes a weighted helmet, air hose, frequently communication lines, and clothing suitable to water temperatures. Unlike the closed-helmet type, in which both helmet and suit are pressurized, only the helmet receives pressurized air. The helmet is open at the bottom (as a bucket inverted) and dependent on internal air pressure to keep the water level below the diver's face. Sudden loss of internal pressure or loss of nearly upright position would result in flooding of the helmet.

All mask- or helmet-type diving rigs dependent on base-supplied air, particularly continuous-flow, have inherent features that would be disadvantageous to sport diving. The main advantages of scuba are its relatively low cost, generally safe use, ease of mobility, and ease of maintenance.

Manufacturer's Instruction Manual

Each manufacturer of the various models of scuba furnishes an instruction manual setting forth recommended procedures for the maintenance, repair, and use of the equipment. The instructions contained in the manual should be carefully studied and fully complied with.

6

SKILLS OF SKIN AND
SCUBA DIVING

Diving with modern breathing equipment may be deceptive because of the ease with which untrained persons can perform under ideal conditions. This attempt might be compared with flying small modern aircraft which are designed in such a way that they almost fly themselves. The operator is safe until an emergency arises. It is then that knowledge, skill, and experience in flying may mean the difference between survival and a serious accident.

A major difference between flying and diving is that in the water the individual may abandon or lose his equipment and still survive with ease providing he is skilled in handling himself in the water. This represents the one and only advantage a skilled diver has over a skilled pilot. An unskilled pilot and an unskilled diver are about equal risks.

Basic personal water skills (or "watermanship") are therefore essential to safe diving with or without breathing apparatus. It is the purpose of this chapter to provide the reader with two safeguards: (1) suggested skills and knowledge for safe diving without breathing apparatus and (2) skills and knowledge which may be considered basic training for an advanced course including the use of scuba. We shall discuss water skills and the use of equipment, and shall introduce activities designed to familiarize the student with these subjects.

Although the skin diver need not equal the competitive swimmer in correct performance of strokes, he should be versatile and at ease in the water. It is interesting to note that although the American crawl is included in many tests preliminary to diving classes, this is the style of swimming least used by divers. Most alert teachers include only those swimming movements which can be performed entirely under the surface. The reason for this seems to be that speed is rarely necessary but power is frequently needed. This power can best be achieved by use of the paired action strokes such as the breaststroke, sidestroke, or modification of the two. Overwater recovery of the arms is rarely possible, since the diver usually is handling various types of gear. Certain water skills have been suggested as minimum for safe and successful skin diving, and should be performed without swim aids of any kind. Since this is not a swimming manual, only the barest description will be given of individual swimming movements. All water work should be done with assigned buddies working together from the beginning of the class.

The potential skin diver should be able to swim and handle himself well in the water. He should have reached a degree of physical and mental development and coordination which makes it possible for him to be safe under most swimming conditions, and he should have a thorough physical examination before entering into a diving class or diving activity.

The classifications following, "General Water Skills," "Personal Safety Skills," "Rescue Skills," and "Skills of Skin Diving," are designed to prepare a relatively weak swimmer for skin diving upon successful completion. Those who have somewhat advanced skills in swimming should demonstrate the specifically recommended swimming movements to the satisfaction of the instructor. It should be noted that the swimming movements recommended are not necessarily orthodox ones, but are made up of combinations of orthodox movements and therefore may be strange to even a skilled swimmer. By following these suggestions the prospective diver should be able to develop a degree of versatility in the water, which is very necessary for safety in diving activities.

Basic Skin Diving

GENERAL WATER SKILLS

Diving without the benefit of an air supply source is a basic skill. Though not complicated by the indirect effects of pressure, as previously described, it still requires the acquisition of theory and development of skills in order to assure safe, intelligent pursuit of the sport. Proficiency attained will materially aid in the later pursuit of scuba diving. The need to develop good techniques is apparent if we visualize the predicament of the scuba diver with air supply exhausted and his base some distance away. Prior planning should preclude such a circumstance but even the best plans sometimes go awry.

The following skills, though common to both skin and scuba diving, are basic. Underwater swimming, breath-holding, and use of the mask, snorkel, and fins, when combined and mastered, will open the door to many underwater pleasures.

Underwater Swimming

It must be remembered that due to water resistance conventional arm strokes will be difficult and inefficient if employed while totally submerged. The following suggestions for alteration and combination of leg and arm strokes will serve as a guide. Practice and personal adaptability will serve to develop proficiency to fit circumstance. As previously mentioned, the use of the hands in underwater activities is usually restricted to the handling of a variety of pieces of equipment or to work being done, so no great emphasis is placed on arm-stroke development.

The scissor or inverted scissor kick. These provide what may be considered the most powerful thrusts available to swimmers. Followed by a glide, they furnish a resting period. The arm stroke used with them may be varied to meet the user's need.

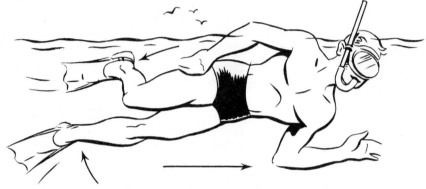

FIG. 28.   SCISSOR KICK, REGULAR OR INVERTED

The breaststroke. The most adaptable of strokes, this one will permit smooth, forward, inplane motion with minimum exertion. Arms are extended forward, then with palms slightly cupped, fingers together, the arms are swept backward to the side, and slightly downward. Recovery is made when the hands reach shoulder level. Arms are brought in to the body, elbows bent, hands under chin. Extension forward is then made and the stroke repeated. This is generally combined with the underwater flutter or dolphin leg strokes.

The elementary backstroke. With the swimmer on his back, the arms are extended to the side just above shoulder level and swept downward to the hips where they are held for a glide. Recovery should be made close to the body in a streamlined motion. Any of the leg actions may be used. This is useful when the diver wishes to rest but still make progress.

The underwater dog paddle. This stroke is so called because of its resemblance to the alternate extension and downward pulling of the forepaws of the swimming dog. Varying degrees of efficiency can be developed, all beginning with the arm extended fully, hand in front of face, fingers together, palm slightly cupped. The pull may then be in a downward sweep, elbow straight or in an elbow-bending pull toward the chest. In either case recovery is made when the hand reaches shoulder or chest level. During recovery motion, the other arm is extended, and repeats the pull as described. Unlike the breaststroke, this arm pull can be adapted to one-hand swimming while carrying equipment in the other or may serve as an aid in towing. It is combined with flutter or scissor kicks.

The "Bicycle Kick"

The bicycle kick is useful when swimming on the back as in towing a float or floating equipment. It will also serve as a rest stroke in open water, since the inverted leg motions provide a sometimes welcome change to leg and thigh muscles.

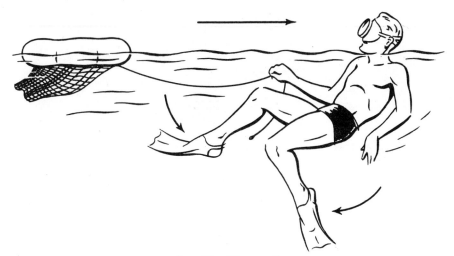

FIG. 29.   "BICYCLE"

Useful with empty scuba.

Basic position of the body is one of semi-sitting or reclining with the head inclined toward the chest to permit breathing through the snorkel. Legs are alternately pushed downward with knee slightly bent and returned upward with a kicking motion from the knee. The kick is most restful when delivered in a wide, slow manner.

The Dolphin Kick

Simulation of the undulating movements of the caudal fin and lower portion of the dolphin's body, after some practice, will provide the diver a strong leg kick. Since forward motion is delivered almost equally on the up as well as on the down phase of the stroke, maximum efficiency can be developed. The following description of movement is basic and will require individual practice in order to develop continuous, smooth, non-tiring propulsion. Initial practice will be best accomplished underwater.

As illustrated, start with the knees slightly bent, toes pointed. Thrust downward by straightening the knees and bending slightly at the waist. The return, or upward, stroke is made with toes pointed, legs straight. About

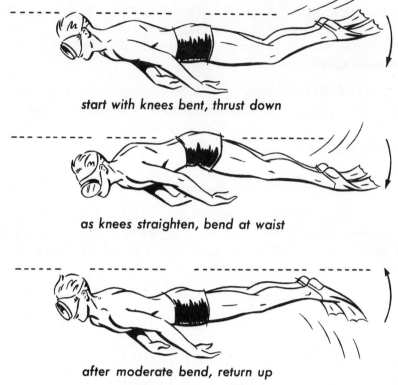

start with knees bent, thrust down

as knees straighten, bend at waist

after moderate bend, return up

Fig. 30.   Dolphin Kick

This is a continuous, slow, waving movement affording fast,
smooth, porpoiselike motion.

halfway up, the knees begin to bend, and at the peak of the stroke are again in the starting position. Avoid extremes in bending the waist or knees. Practice will bring about a slight flip of the fins at the peak of upward and downward motions, affording additional thrust. The latter is accomplished by ankle movement and will come with the development of timing.

Personal Safety Skills

Sculling

This is a useful skill in treading water and holding position on the surface or underwater. One or both hands may be used. Palms are slightly cupped while hands are moved in a figure-eight motion. Thumbs are up on motion toward body and down when moving away. The resultant angle of the palm in motion serves as a lifting plane. Experimentation will prove this to be an efficient, versatile, energy-conserving stroke.

Treading Water

Although both legs and one or both hands can be used in treading water, the diver should be able to maintain himself upright using his legs only. (This may be necessary when placing game in a sack, draining or adjusting a leaking mask, or pursuing other activity requiring the use of the hands.) This can be accomplished by using a slow scissors kick, a slow, wide flutter kick, or modified sculling motions with the fins.

ACTIVITY: (1) Practice treading water with hands alone, legs alone and then with legs and one hand. (2) Tread water for several minutes with legs alone, holding hands clear of water. Experiment with combinations of leg kicks and hand sculling.

Floating or Resting in a Floating Position

Most people can float with help and practice. Those with negative buoyancy may find it necessary to use gentle movements of the arms and legs. This is a very important self-rescue skill. With a snorkel, floating can be done face down.

ACTIVITY: Experiment and practice.

RESCUE SKILLS

Prevention of accidents by careful planning, preparation, and always diving with a competent buddy is of equal importance with knowing what to do in case of emergency. Whether diving with a group or as a single pair the practice of knowing where your "buddy" is and staying within communication distance (visual or audible) may serve to avert a regrettable incident.

It should be realized that rescue problems involving divers may be quite different from those involving swimmers. Much diving activity takes place in areas not normally used for recreational swimming. These areas may be characterized by rocks, reefs, marine animals or plants, and unusual currents or surges, generally or around wrecks. Many are far from any organized lifeguard or beach protection service. Many are remote, with no normal access routes. It is therefore quite necessary that divers learn and practice rescue skills and first aid measures (Chapter 7 is devoted to first aid). Every diver should acquire a working knowledge of life saving techniques, briefly summarized here.

General Pointers

It is most desirable that the rescuer avoid personal contact with the distressed diver if at all possible. In many cases the victim can be talked into helping himself. The rescuer should push the float to the victim and instruct or help him to hang on. Most distressed divers or swimmers merely need a rest and an opportunity to recover from panic.

If it becomes necessary to perform a swimming rescue or recovery from the bottom, avoid fighting with the distressed person. Approach and make contact from the rear. Make the rescue with maximum safety to yourself. Removal of the victim's weight belt will materially aid in keeping him afloat. Inflation of a personal flotation device will also aid. Removal of the face mask is not necessary unless artificial respiration has to be performed. Water breathed in through the nose will cause spasmodic choking and coughing more readily than when water and air are taken in through the mouth.

Towing Methods

Towing methods as taught and practiced in normal swimmer rescue may be difficult if not impossible to employ in the rescue of a distressed scuba diver. Strapped-on equipment, weight belt, flotation devices, and open water conditions may make other methods more desirable. Several methods are suggested:

The arm tow. Grasp the hand, wrist, or forearm—left to left or right to right—and twist it slightly outward and upward so as to help arch or surface the victim's body. Keep your and his arm as fully extended as possible while you swim on your side. Observe his condition during the tow to base.

The clothing, equipment, or hair tow. If the distressed diver or swimmer is wearing clothing or strapped-on equipment, the rescuer can grasp it with one hand near the back of the neck and tow him in face-up position to the float or boat. If no equipment or clothing is available and the hair is long enough, it may supply a useful handle for towing if it is grabbed near the forehead. Tow with arm fully extended.

NOTE: Avoid fighting with the distressed diver. Make the rescue with maximum safety to yourself. In all cases remove weights and, if necessary, mask.

SKILLS OF SKIN DIVING

Submerging

Head-first surface dive. If properly performed, this dive will permit the diver to drop a couple of body lengths before beginning to swim. The dive should be started with some forward motion on the surface. When the dive point is nearly reached, the head should be bent downward, the hands brought to the area of the hip and palms facing downward. The body is bent at the waist and the hands swept toward the head. The legs may be extended above the water at this point by straightening the body and legs when the body is vertical. An alternate method is to pull the legs into a tuck position and, when the body is vertical, straighten the legs above water. The latter unless practiced is more splashy but generally delivers greater downward push. Hands and arms move to extended position to protect the head. When downward motion slows, start kicking to the desired depth.

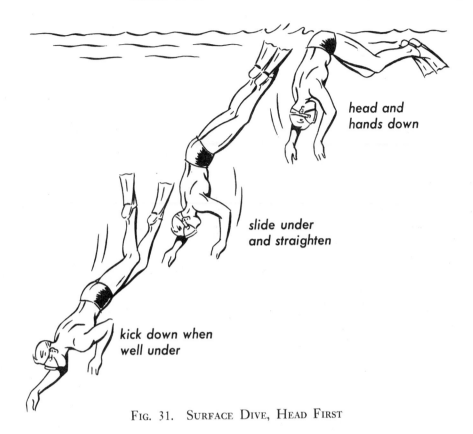

head and
hands down

slide under
and straighten

kick down when
well under

Fig. 31. Surface Dive, Head First

Feet-first surface dive, or "vertical drop dive." When practiced and perfected, this maneuver permits dropping nearly straight down from the surface without the need for forward motion. The feet-first attitude gives added protection when water depth is not known or obstructions or heavy concentration of water plants exist in the dive area. Neutral or slightly negative buoyancy acquired during descent may eliminate the need for reversal of position and permit full drop feet first.

Starting from an upright position (as in treading water), give a strong kick with the fins and, if possible, a downward stroke with the hands to lift the body upward above the surface. Immediately following the lift, straighten the legs, body, and hands, as illustrated in Figure 32. This attitude is maintained as long as downward motion continues. Leveling off or reversal of position as indicated will facilitate further sloping or vertical descent.

ACTIVITY: Practicing both of the preceding surface dives while recovering a heavy object from the deepest part of the pool will help to determine the merits of each. Practice hyperventilation before each dive and vary the ascent from vertical to long slopes. Don't exceed comfortable breath-holding limits (not more than a few extra breaths).

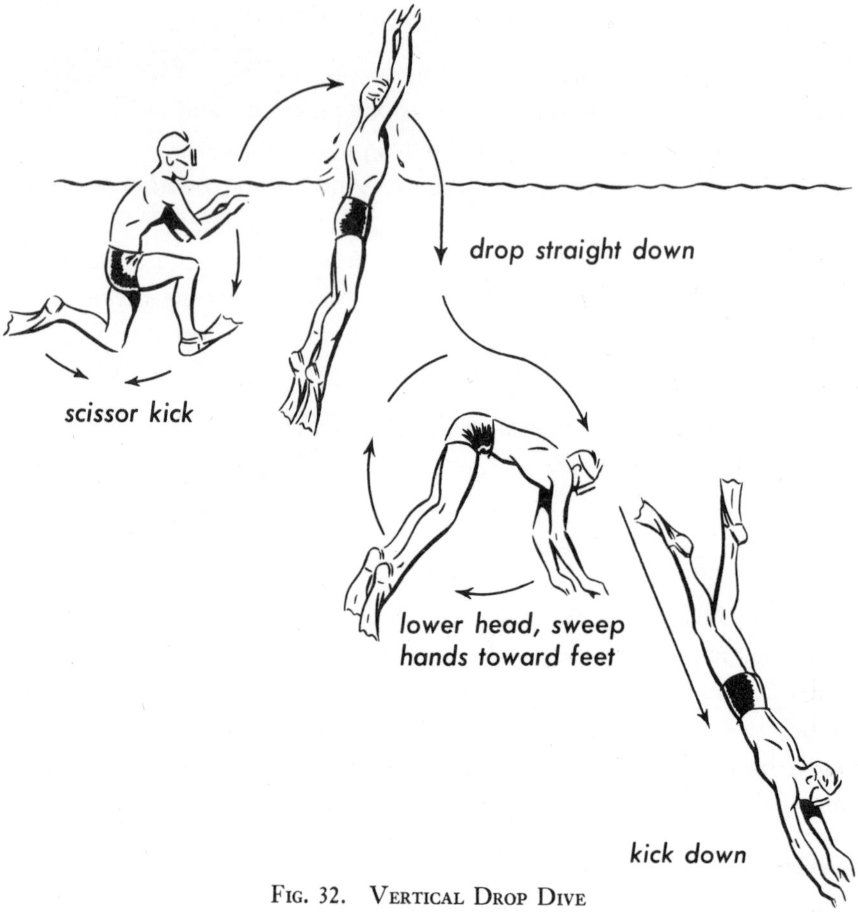

drop straight down

scissor kick

lower head, sweep
hands toward feet

kick down

FIG. 32.   VERTICAL DROP DIVE

Underwater Swimming

The underwater breaststroke. The arms are extended in front of the face and swept almost to the hips, where they may be held for a short glide. They are then recovered in a streamlined motion to in front of the face again. They may be held here for a short glide again or immediately swept back for the stroke. Any effective leg stroke may be used.

Dark water stroke. It must be remembered that the use of the above-described arm strokes underwater is not advisable when visibility is poor. The hands should be *touching and extended forward* so as to protect the head and face from unseen obstacles. Mobility should be necessarily slowed and safety enhanced. Leg strokes will provide sufficient propulsion.

ACTIVITY: Experiment and practice all the strokes above. Notice that without flippers most swimmers find the flutter kick less effective than the other leg strokes.

Breath-Holding

As described in Chapter 3 "Nothing to Breathe" is a skill to be acquired through practice. Few persons can, without practice, hold their breath for more than about fifteen seconds without a good deal of effort. Practice and hyperventilation will increase the time to about a minute without producing any noticeable effects. Read and heed the above reference lest you push the limits too far. Breath-holding contests and long-distance underwater swimming are inadvisable and serve no useful purpose. Hyperventilation prior to diving from the surface will provide safe comfort during the dive within reasonable limits. A reasonable interval between dives should be allowed.

NOTE: Breath-holding or underwater distance-swimming contests should not be permitted. Contestants are likely to overexert under these conditions, and no advantage can be found in these activities.

THE MASK

The face mask is an essential piece of equipment in both skin and scuba diving. Selection and assurance of proper fit are described in Chapter 5. It is advisable to familiarize yourself with the peculiarities of the mask you purchase before you attempt full use of it. Defogging, clearing, and maintaining pressure balance with ambient pressures should be practiced until they become habit. Following are suggested activities:

Preparation

Adjust the head strap so that the mask will be held gently but firmly in place. Do not attempt to seal an improperly fitted mask by drastically tightening the head strap. Determination of fit should be made before purchase. After adjustments, apply a fog preventative, such as saliva, seaweed, tobacco, raw potato, or one of the commercial preparations to the inside of the lens. Rinse or follow the manufacturer's directions.

Pressure Equalization

Swim with the mask on. Dive to the bottom at several depths, and as the mask is pressed to the face by water pressure, exhale lightly from the nose until pressures balance. Over-correction will result in escape of air. Under-correction is apparent with continued feeling of tightness.

Clearing

Flood the mask by lifting one edge of the skirt. While in a number of different positions, exhale slowly into the mask. Note where the air escapes in each position. Even when equipped with a purge valve, the air will escape unless some portion of the mask is held to the face.

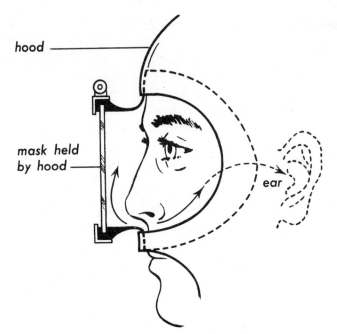

FIG. 33. EQUALIZING PRESSURE IN FULL HOOD AND MASK

Having noted that the injected air will usually escape on the "up" part of the mask, you may now go about clearing the flooded mask in one of the following ways:

Horizontal roll. While in a horizontal position, place the palm of the right hand on the right side of the lens rim, thumb, and forefinger on the skirt. Apply only sufficient pressure toward the face as to assure a firm seal. Start to exhale slowly into the mask while dropping the left shoulder to start

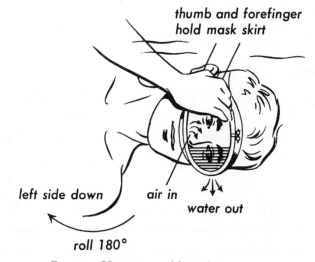

FIG. 34. HORIZONTAL MASK CLEARING

the horizontal roll. Air displaces water. Continue the roll, maintaining the horizontal attitude until water level drops below the left eye. Continuing the roll for 180 degrees will completely clear most masks. Full-face masks (entire face enclosed) may be cleared in a similar manner without the probability of water remaining as in other methods.

FIG. 35.   MASK AND HOSE CLEARING

Vertical tilt. While in a vertical position gently press the upper portion of the mask toward the face to assure good seal at the forehead and eye area. Start gentle exhalation into the mask. As the water is being gradually forced out, tilt the head backward looking toward the surface. Continue until the mask is cleared.

Practice will be necessary to determine the best tilt angle and rate of exhalation. These are variable due to the variety of mask design and of adaptability of the individual.

Purge valve and nose pinch masks. Since "purging" valves are installed in the lens, skirt or at the base of a nose pocket, some experimentation may be necessary before satisfactory clearing is achieved when in various positions.

Nose pinch pockets built into the skirt or a full nose enclosure are a convenience to permit sealing the nose in order to equalize ear and sinus pressures when preventing "squeeze." Rarely do these devices present any difficulty that isn't overcome by a little experimentation.

USING THE FINS

Selection of the type and size fins best adapted to your physique and muscle development, as suggested in Chapter 5, will facilitate learning to use them to best advantage. Keep in mind that maximum result with minimum expenditure of energy is the goal, not speed.

Donning

Wetting the feet and fins will aid. Hold side ribs of the fin and insert the foot all the way into the pocket in either open heel or slipper type. If the fit is correct, the heel strap or back lip of the slipper can then be placed over the ankle with little or no stretching.

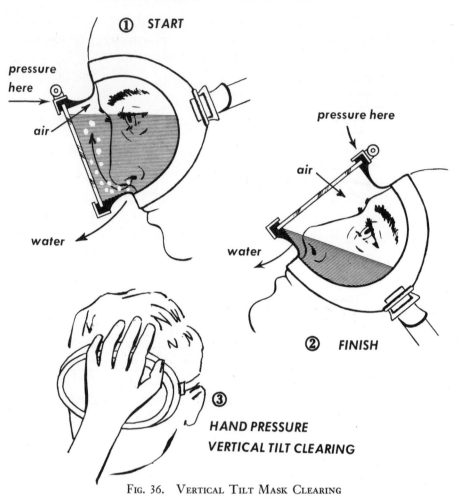

FIG. 36.   VERTICAL TILT MASK CLEARING

Don't attempt to walk around with fins on. Even with practice, it's still a clumsy maneuver. If necessary in later diving circumstances, it will be found that walking backward (in or out of water) is much less hazardous.

ACTIVITY:

1. After donning face mask and fins, hold on to the side of the pool, body erect. Move the fins backward and forward, varying width of kick and looseness of knee and ankle. Note the point at which the most lift appears when performing this reasonably slow, wide kick. Now turn on your side in horizontal attitude. Try both regular and reverse scissors. Note that if the legs pass (contrary to usual form), little if any loss of forward drive results. Experiment with the simultaneous motion of the legs and thighs as described in the dolphin kick. This may be a little disappointing at first, since the results will be rather splashy. Experimentation with the frog kick will demonstrate efficiency loss and general impracticability when wearing fins.

NOSE "PURGE" VALVE

pressure

to clear: position valve face
toward bottom; exhale
while applying sealing
pressure on upper rim.

PURGE VALVE IN LENS

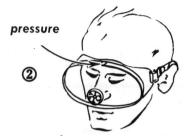

pressure

to clear: press upper rim
(valve toward bottom at first);
exhale; raise.

NOSE "PINCH" POCKETS IN SKIRT

thumb, forefinger or both index
fingers (preferred);
compress nostrils for ear clearing.

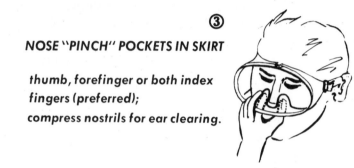

FIG. 37. FACE MASK "PURGING" VALVES

2. Cast off and give each type kick a thorough test by using fins only. Hands and arms can be used as diving planes or trailed at the sides. Again, vary the rate, width, and looseness of the kicks. Experiment with kicks while on back, side, and face down. Pay particular attention to and avoid continued use of kick variations which tend to tighten or cramp leg, thigh, or back muscles.

3. If there is opportunity, it may be to your advantage to try other types or sizes (fin area). You will find it advantageous to observe and be observed by others while learning. Comparisons and constructive criticism will help to perfect fin use.

NOTE: If neoprene boots or "flipper slippers" are worn with the fins, remove the fins and try various kicks (in shallow water). You will find considerable loss of efficiency and even less drive than afforded by bare feet. Loss or removal of fins while wearing most types of boots will necessitate using arm strokes for support or propulsion.

Heavy athletic socks will provide protection from chafing and do not drastically reduce kick efficiency when fins are removed.

USING THE SNORKEL

The major problem to be overcome is clearing of the snorkel after diving. Beginners frequently breathe small amounts of water left in the tube because of incomplete clearing. This results in a spasm of choking and gagging.

Most snorkels are equipped with a device for attachment to the mask strap. Attaching it on the left side will serve to keep it clear of the air hose when using single hose scuba. Whether on left or right, such attachment is generally advisable so as to permit easy access, proper positioning and prevention of loss.

ACTIVITY: Don mask, snorkel and fins.

1. Insert the mouthpiece. The wide flange goes between the lips and teeth. The smaller flange goes inside the teeth. The small collar or projecting knobs are held *lightly* between the teeth. Breathe through the tube; accustom yourself to the breathing effort noticed. Immerse the face mask; breathe. Continue to lower the head while cautiously breathing. When the tip of the snorkel is immersed, the tube will fill but water does *not* enter the mouth *unless* you ignore the filling and take another breath. Practice blowing the tube clear by using a quick, forceful, short "puff." The "puff" method will permit a second clearing attempt without taking another breath.

2. In shoulder deep water, flood the face mask. Breathe through the snorkel with mask flooded. Squat down so as to bring the snorkel below the surface. Using the "vertical tilt" method, clear the mask. Rise until the mask is just below the surface, then puff the snorkel clear. Inhale cautiously after clearing. Clearing both the mask and snorkel on one breath may take some practice. It can be done easily when the air volume exhaled is nearly equal to mask and snorkel volume.

3. Practice surface dives and snorkel clearing. Practice surface swimming and adjust the snorkel position to permit continuous breathing. Practice retrieving mask and snorkel from the bottom. Don and clear both.

THE WEIGHT BELT

Since "neutral" buoyancy is desirable in both skin and scuba diving, many divers must resort to making themselves heavier. This necessitates the use of a weight belt equipped with a *quick-release* type buckle or double "D" rings with a *safety hitch*.

Determine the amount of weight you need by stringing ten 1-pound weights on a line. Take a *deep breath* and dive with the weights. While on the bottom, remove one of the weights at a time until you become slightly buoyant. The amount of weight retained on the line should be sufficient to give you desired buoyancy when diving on a normal breath.

Practice quick removal of the belt. Practice *safety hitch*.

The foregoing has assumed that only the equipment described was being worn. It must be noted and thoroughly impressed on the diver that WEIGHT BELTS MUST BE WORN OUTSIDE OF PROTECTIVE CLOTHING AND ANY OTHER EQUIPMENT REQUIRING HARNESS. THE QUICK-RELEASE DEVICE MUST BE READILY AVAILABLE FOR "LAST ON—FIRST OFF" USE.

ACTIVITY: Completion of mastering basic equipment so far described will put you on the road to enjoyment of skin diving in open water and to greater depths than in a pool. Review of the lesson plans in the latter section of this chapter will materially aid in acquiring ease and confidence.

Light refraction and restricted peripheral vision will create conditions peculiar to underwater vision. The enlargement of objects, deceptive distances, and relatively small area of vision may be compensated for by practice and familiarity. Practice searching for a variety of objects. Observe magnified size. Discover how easy it is to miss finding some of the objects. Occupation with a variety of simple tasks will tend to put you at ease and to lessen concentration on the task of submerging and surfacing.

Methods of Entry and Exit

Up to this point, most every activity started in the pool. Future activities may be started from boats, floats, docks, or rocky ledges. Since equipment worn makes the familiar head-first dive impractical, the basic entries given here should be practiced.

With all gear in place, hold the face mask firmly with one hand covering the lens. Later on, when using scuba, it may be desirable under some conditions to also hold the lower part of the tank harness so as to prevent upward collision with neck or head. Most entries are made from a few feet above the surface, so the following will suffice:

Front jump—feet first and together. Designed for immediate descent in water of sufficient depth and clarity.

Front step—feet first with legs spread wide, as in a long stride. When the fins touch the surface the legs are brought quickly together, toes of fins pointed, as in a kicking stroke. Downward motion is stopped, after a little practice, before head and shoulders are submerged.

Forward roll—With body bent or crouched, roll forward so as to enter when slightly less than half of a front somersault is reached. Avoid springing upward or doing a full flip.

Standing back entry—With back to water and knowledge that no one is under you, the jump or step-off methods used in front entry may be made in reverse.

Back roll—From a crouched or sitting position close to the surface, merely roll backward. Care and practice should be exercised when making this type entry, as straightening or opening up too quickly could result in bumping the head on the wall, boat, or float.

Exit—If to be up a boarding ladder or over rocks, it will be much easier if the fins are removed prior to climbing.

Since entry from or exit to a moving boat or float, as practiced by military divers, is hardly justifiable in sport diving, it has been given no space here.

Advanced Skin Diving

Having mastered the basic skills and acquired familiarity with equipment, the new diver will want to move to open water. Initial enjoyment of nearly weightless exploration of the water world will be followed by desire to accomplish more than mere sightseeing.

Dependent upon the desires of the individual, many underwater activities can be pursued. Some will require additional skills, technical knowledge, and adaptation of land techniques to underwater conditions, and all will be better accomplished if basic diving skills are perfected to the point of habit. Reference to the Chapter 5, "Basic Skin and Scuba Equipment," and the many available publications dealing with skin and scuba diving will supply an ample field of activities. Special skills, technical knowledge, and knowledge of environmental data along with detailed instructions for use of supplementary equipment can be acquired with specific research.

The basic nature of this manual limits discussion of such supplements to mere mention. Experience and progress into specific diving fields will place many of the "supplements" in the category of "necessary" equipment. Knives, prying tools, watches, depth gauges, compass, thermometer, decompression indicator, camera, spear gun, to mention a few, all have general or specific use in some instances. Thoughtful planning will indicate which are needed and which will be excess baggage.

EQUIPMENT AND CLOTHING FOR ADVANCED DIVING

When the diver progresses from the training area to open-water conditions, several items of equipment will be added to the basics: flotation devices, both personal and of base type (both discussed in Chapter 5); a knife, not for hunting but invaluable as a necessary tool in many diving circumstances; protective clothing of some type, also previously described and a necessity in cold water. Since the latter involves several types and familiarization before choice and use, the following suggestions may serve to aid in the choice as well as initial familiarization.

Wet Suits

The most popular and easiest to maintain, these present few problems. Properly filling out the measurement chart supplied by most suit fabricators when ordering should insure the required comfortable, snug (not too tight) fit of all components. Hood, jacket, pants, gloves, and boots are the complete outfit. Since the designed function includes the presence of some water, all or any combination of parts may be worn to fit the need. Dependent upon the thickness of the material chosen and parts worn, buoyancy will be noticeably increased. Increasing the number of weights on the belt until the desired neutral state is obtained should be done while wearing all components, combinations, and the jacket alone. Be sure to *allow the escape of trapped air* by manipulation of the suit parts and alteration of body positions in such a manner as to force air to flow upward and out of the openings. Note the amount of weight required for each combination.

Some loss of buoyancy will occur during a dive, due to compression of gas-filled cells in the suit material. Experience will indicate any desired adjustments to fit dive circumstances.

REMEMBER: There will be considerable difference in weights required for neutral buoyancy in fresh or salt water.

Absorbent Clothing

Such items as long underwear, sweaters, sweat shirts, or other cloth garments suitable to provide insulation can be worn. Although heavy and cold when worn wet, out of water, these garments insulate against heat loss with variable efficiency. They generally increase buoyancy. Appropriate weight compensation after elimination of trapped air will be necessary. Efficiency does not compare with that of a good wet or dry suit. As in all diving in cold water, whether protected or not, be alert to signs of chilling and give them heed.

Dry Suits

These require complete exclusion of water if maximum efficiency and safety is to be obtained. Having chosen the dry suit and the appropriate undergarments, you should practice donning and sealing the suit, as required, before going into the water. Ample talcum powder to facilitate entry, and short fingernails to prevent tearing are prerequisites. After learning the best way to don and seal, you should make the following pool or shallow water experiments, for the knowledge you will gain from them may be invaluable later on.

1. Enter the water gradually in a vertical, head-up position. Permit air to escape (without letting water in) by stretching the uppermost opening at the neck or face (if hood is attached). Release air from arms in similar manner by stretching open the wrist cuff.
2. Note the buoyant effect attained, even with air excluded. Add weights to belt until the desired neutral state is attained.
3. In warm chest-deep water, without weights, deliberately flood the suit. Note the change in buoyancy. Swim in shallow water, noting the difficulties. Now don the weight belt and note the extreme loss of buoyancy.

The above will tend to illustrate the need for proper sealing and regular examination of the thin rubber to detect holes. Unlike the wet suit, where a hole only involves some loss of heat and negligible loss of buoyancy, a hole in the dry suit produces considerable loss of insulation, buoyancy, and swimming efficiency.

NOTE: Air not excluded from the dry suit, which also envelopes the feet, may concentrate there during a head-first descent. The result may necessitate a swimming somersault maneuver to shift the air before a head-first ascent can be made.

Use of the Main Types of Scuba

Having mastered skin diving techniques, which should be considered essential and basic to survival in all free diving pursuits, you are now in position to advance to the use of scuba. There is, as previously described in Chapter 5, more than one type. Each has its own techniques due to construction variation.

Closed-circuit and semiclosed-circuit scuba techniques will not be discussed since they are not considered adaptable to sport diving. Their employment is usually restricted to specialized occupations or purpose, and techniques and training for using them require specific, intense supervision by highly qualified specialists in that field.

Open-circuit scuba types, as described, include double-hose units of one- or two-stage demand regulator design. The two-stage single-hose units may be of the mouthpiece or the full-face mask design.

All of the aforementioned have some things in common and will be discussed generally. The single-hose designs must receive special consideration since the full-face mask unit presents special problems. All that are pertinent to the equipment owned or available for use must be considered essential to safe usage. Each technique should be reviewed and practiced until it becomes as natural as everyday living. The following summation of essential knowledge will prepare you for the specific and general coverage which follows in the form of discussion, instruction, and illustration.

1. Know how your equipment operates (see Chapter 5).
2. Know when the equipment should and should not be used (mechanically, Chapter 5; physically, Chapter 3; environmentally, Chapter 8).
3. Know how to clear scuba units while submerged (Chapter 6).
4. Know the importance of breathing normally, but cautiously after clearing double-hose, single-hose, or full-face mask scuba.
5. Be thoroughly familiar with doff and don procedures both on deck and when submerged (Chapter 6).
6. Know how to clear mouthpieces, hoses, or full masks of all scuba that you use or may use on special occasion.
7. Know and habitually perform predive check of equipment, diver, and dive plan (all chapters).

A predive check of equipment must be made before using (Chapter 5, p. 111, Chapter 9, pp. 207–8).

Although the general treatment here relates to the double-hose type of scuba, the text and illustrations are such that adaptation to the single-hose type is easily made.

The increased populariy of the two-stage single-hose regulator is well deserved. Enumeration of all its advantages and/or disadvantages is best left to the myriad of experienced divers rather than to this text. The ease with which the mouthpiece can be cleared, absence of "free flow," construction of second-stage demand valve and exhaust port will permit alteration, within limits, of many techniques pictured in this chapter. The addition of pertinent illustrations should serve to guide the diver learning to use this type of scuba.

Starting in shallow water, learn to clear hose and/or full mask units as a necessary skill in case they become flooded. The first step in learning this technique (hose unit) is to remember that the exhaust hose is on your left (in standard equipment). In order to clear water out you must roll left side down and exhale vigorously. Breathe shallowly to test. If some water still remains, repeat roll and blow. Practice until you can do this with ease.

Another method is to roll over on your back holding the mouthpiece up. This produces a constant flow with air replacing the water. All you have to do then (see Figure 39), as you are still on your back, is to put the mouthpiece into your mouth, roll to the right into prone position, and swim on.

With this knowledge you can proceed to the next step: doffing and donning the rig underwater.

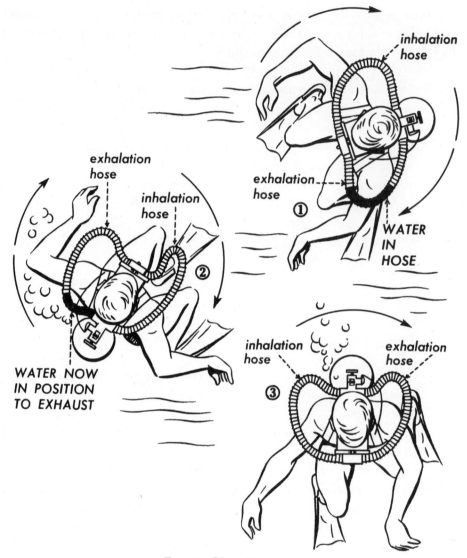

FIG. 38.   HOSE CLEARING

Maintaining a horizontal position, drop left shoulder and follow through with
a deliberate 360-degree roll as shown. (If swimming conditions do not permit
the roll to be completed, Position 1 allows diver to breathe water-free air.)
When Position 2 is reached start exhaling vigorously. Continue exhalation until
roll is completed (3). Resume normal breathing.

SCUBA DOFF AND DON

Procedures illustrated may be altered as needed to fit the diver's physique or adaptability. The sitting position may be replaced by kneeling (one
knee up, one on bottom). The weight belt is draped across the horizontal
thigh during doffing or donning. The kneeling position, if used with double-
hose scuba, requires more care in preventing free flow due to probable distance between mouthpiece and regulator.

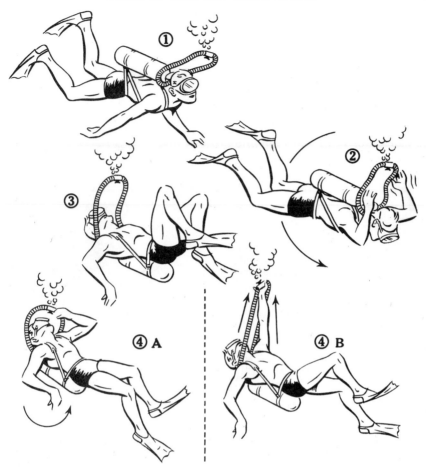

FIG. 39. REGAINING MOUTHPIECE

Roll on back (3); if air is flowing freely readjust mouthpiece and relax, taking a few breaths (4A); if air is not flowing freely, which indicates that the regulator is flooded, grasp and squeeze off the exhalation hose near the mouthpiece and extend the hose upward with several quick jerks, rotating the mouthpiece up as you extend it (4B); when air starts to flow put the bit in your mouth and relax with a few breaths, as in 4A.

Either the sitting or kneeling position can be assumed in doffing or donning the single-hose type scuba. Unlike the double-hose type, the single-hose scuba can be doffed or donned in a manner similar to putting on a coat. Shoulder harness may be adjusted and fastened prior to donning. The right side is donned first. Doffing the unit by this method is best accomplished if the left shoulder harness is removed first. Since there should be no free-flow problem in single-hose scuba, there is no need to keep mouthpiece and tank valve at nearly the same level.

Scuba doff and don procedures will serve to develop underwater thinking and necessary tactile familiarity with the associated harness.

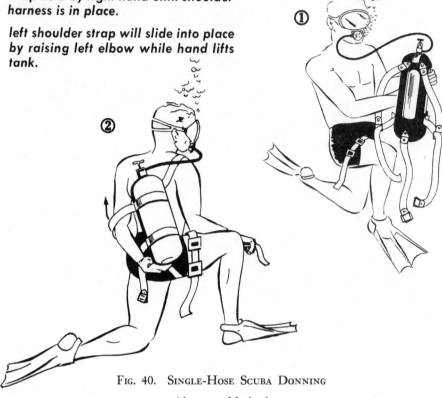

tank held by left hand
right forearm through
shoulder strap.

right shoulder strap on first

crotch strap and right side of waist
strap held by right hand until shoulder
harness is in place.

left shoulder strap will slide into place
by raising left elbow while hand lifts
tank.

FIG. 40.   SINGLE-HOSE SCUBA DONNING
Alternate Method

ACTIVITIES: Trade scuba units one diver to another, either or both equipped (skin diver, scuba diver exchange illustrated). Doffing a unit and donning another which is suspended by a line, midway between top and bottom, will simulate conditions encountered when taking long decompression stops. Doff and don all diving gear to develop orderly progression of action in order of importance to survival.

REMEMBER: ALL HARNESS FASTENINGS SHOULD BE OF THE QUICK-RELEASE TYPE. WEIGHT BELT GOES ON LAST AND OFF FIRST. BREATHE FIRST, THEN DON THE GEAR. EXHALE ALL THE WAY UP AFTER DOFFING SCUBA. THINK BEFORE YOU ACT.

BUDDY BREATHING

No matter how carefully planned the dive may be, unforeseen mechanical failure or excessive demands on the air supply may make it necessary for

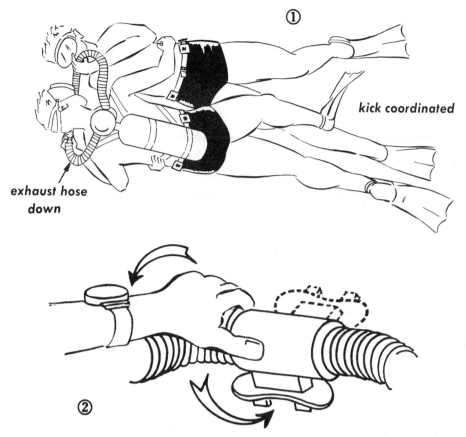

reversal of mouthpiece during double-hose buddy breathing transfer

Fig. 41. Double-Hose Scuba Buddy Breathing

Hose held by left hand of each diver near mouthpiece

divers to share a single air supply. Emergency ascents may be more safely accomplished if the need for "free" or "buoyant" ascents is eliminated. After some practice in a variety of positions, using either single- or double-hose scuba, nearly normal breathing cycles will be achieved by both divers. Initial practice in shoulder-deep water, kneeling or lying on the bottom face to face, while learning to transfer the mouthpiece and clearing methods, will better prepare both divers for eventual swimming and ascent sharing of the single air supply.

Horizontal or swimming position sharing will be best accomplished if the supplying hose is toward the surface. Double-hose scuba transfer in either vertical or horizontal position is generally uncomplicated because the mouthpiece need only be turned over to accommodate the sharing diver. Single-hose transfer is a little more complicated because of the necessity to keep the exhaust port in the area of the chin. The airless diver grasps the hose side of the mouthpiece assembly with the left hand, palm toward the donor. The hand is turned, palm toward the receiver during the transfer. This action puts the mouthpiece in correct position. The hose will have an "S" bend in it. Both purging button use and "puff" exhalation clearing should be practiced.

Coordination of movement and close contact will be facilitated if both divers maintain contact by holding with the free *right* hand. This contact may be utilized to signal need for exchange or other action.

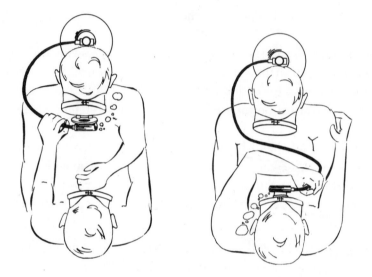

FIG. 42.   SINGLE-HOSE SCUBA BUDDY BREATHING

Buddy Breathing During Ascent

SPECIAL CAUTION MUST BE OBSERVED DURING AN ASCENT WHILE BUDDY BREATHING. Since the ascent should be at a regular rate (60 feet per minute) and the breathing rate somewhat less than normal, THERE MUST BE CONTINUAL EXHALATION BETWEEN INHALATIONS DURING THE ENTIRE ASCENT. The exhalation may be controlled and minimal but of such character that AN OPEN AIRWAY IS MAINTAINED AT ALL TIMES.

All these skills should be accomplished in shallow water before going into deep water.

The method of clearing the mask while using the snorkel has been mentioned. Clearing the mask with the unit on is much easier, for then you have all the air you need.

FULL-FACE PLATE UNIT

Although scuba equipped with a full-face mask is not among the more popular types, it will be covered very briefly here. Most of these devices are of the two-stage demand-regulator type. The first stage, or high-pressure reducer, is generally located at the tank valve and as in most, reduces tank pressure to approximately 100 psi over ambient pressure. A single high-pressure hose connects it to the second stage, which is usually located on and an integral part of the full-face mask. This demand valve, purging device, and "air economizer tube" are located on the right side with air entry designed to cross the eye area of the face plate so as to reduce fogging.

Clearing of the flooded mask by both breathing and purge button methods should be practiced. The following method is generally adaptable to most such units.

Put the unit on and try it in shallow water. Then swim around to deeper water and return to shallower water. To clear the mask, duck under and let water enter the mask by raising up one edge. Roll head and body so that left side of mask is toward bottom. Place thumb and forefinger of right hand on skirt of mask in area of regulator; this places palm over the purging button. Place a finger of left hand between face and lip of mask near exhaust valve on left to let water escape. Now, either by gently exhaling or by pressing purging button with palm of right hand, replace water with air. When water level is below left eye, you know that you can inhale cautiously through your mouth.

NOTE: Use of purging button is often accompanied by inability to inhale *because* you simply forgot to exhale.

Practice in shallow water until this is done easily; then practice flooding and clearing while swimming with unit on.

On the full-face plate unit there is a small tube on the right called an "Air Economizer." This can be used like a snorkel when on the surface, but must be closed before submerging. Using the "Air Economizer" will conserve air in tank. This tube can also be used for nursing underwater. When it is opened, the other persons can place their mouths over it and breathe in and out as they did with the mouthpiece unit. All this can be done while one

FIG. 43. SAVE AIR WITH A SNORKEL

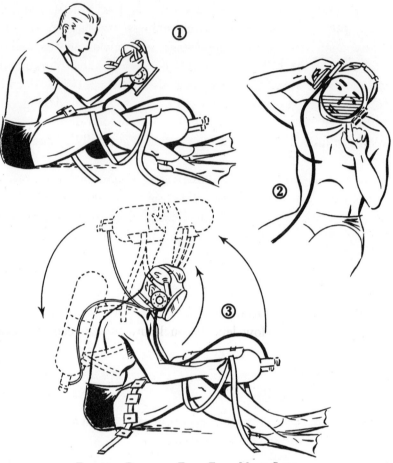

FIG. 44.   DONNING FULL-FACE MASK SCUBA

(1) Surface dive or drop feet first to unit when you have a mental picture of the donning procedure. Assume a sitting position with valve toward feet, and grip tank with legs. Slip on the mask—be sure it is straight—and tighten the lower straps.

(2) Bend forward and turn your head so that your chin is toward your right shoulder. The exhaust valve on the left side of the mask is now the lowest part. With thumb and forefinger of the right hand pressing the right edge of mask to your face, press the purging button with palm. Lifting edge of mask adjacent to the exhaust valve slightly with finger of left hand will allow water to be forced out. Look toward exhaust valve—*you can see last of water go out.* Remove left finger as soon as water level is below left eye, allowing remainder to go out valve. Exhale and inhale shallowly to test. Adjust mask and repeat clearing if water seeps in. Transfer weights to thighs.

(3) Reach through shoulder harness and grasp tank with both hands. Swing tank over head to back, smooth end close to head. Shoulder harness drops in place. Check air line (turning mask over in doffing or donning will cause it to kink) before fastening waist belt. When everything is checked put on weight belt.

Clearing the mask is easily done while in a prone swimming position by merely repeating the head roll described above in Step 2. (Doff and Don developed by Subcommittee, YMCA, Washington, D.C.)

FIG. 45. DOFFING HOSE TYPE SCUBA
(1) Remove the weight belt and drape it across your thighs. This will permit you to sit on the bottom. Unfasten harness. Free crotch strap. (2) Reach back with both hands. Grasp tank. Keeping regulator close to your head, bring the unit to the legs. Hold with knees. Bend forward and breathe shallowly. Transfer weight belt to tank at lower end. (3) With face close to regulator, shift legs away from unit. Hold tank at weights to prevent floating upward while you stretch out. (4) Now take a half-breath and remove the mouthpiece. Tuck mouthpiece between regulator and tank valve. As a complete training exercise the face mask would be removed at this time and placed beside the regulator.

FIG. 46. DONNING HOSE TYPE SCUBA

(1) Surface dive or drop feet first to unit. Before returning to the unit you should review in your mind each step to be followed in donning. (2) Grasp the unit (to hold you down). Remove the mouthpiece and raise to allow free flow of air. Insert in mouth. With exhaust hose low, exhale sharply to clear water. Now breathe shallowly to test. Repeat if necessary. Bring face close to regulator and begin to swing legs forward to sitting position. (3) Complete sitting position. Grasp tank with your knees. Transfer weights to thighs. (Don and clear mask if removed.) Adjust harness for ease in donning.

(4) Grasp tank near regulator with both hands and pass in an arc (regulator close to head) to position on back. Sitting on the crotch strap will hold the unit in position and allow you to work with both hands. Fasten harness— be sure to use safety hitches. Prior knowledge of harness parts and arrangement is a *must* for rapid donning. Now don the weight belt, and you are ready to go. Repeated practice will make donning possible under more adverse conditions. (Credit for this Doff and Don goes to Los Angeles County, Department of Parks and Recreation, Los Angeles, California.)

person has this unit on or it can be passed around. The "Air Economizer" does not have to be cleared because there is a constant flow of air from it when opened underwater.

To don the unit underwater, first put the mask on, then tighten all straps, beginning with bottom pair. Clear the water out as described above. Do all this before actually putting the cylinders on your back.

NOTE: For safety, do all your learning in the shallow end of a pool first. Be able to do it with ease before attempting to do it in deeper water. When you have mastered all the skills, you are better prepared to go into open water. But never go by yourself. And leave deep diving for the professionals —they get paid for it.

Before attempting open-water dives, practice rescue of a buddy using a float, inner tube, or surfboard. Learn how to perform mouth-to-mouth artificial respiration (see Chapter 7, "First Aid for Diving Accidents"). Practice dark-water diving by covering inside face plate with cardboard. Keep your hands together, arms extended, while you search for an object or try to find your way to a particular spot. Have a buddy over you as a safety man.

Checklist for Skin and Scuba Skills
USE THIS LIST TO CHECK YOURSELF ON ALL SKILLS

1. FINS
   - a. Comfortable Fit ☐
   - b. Wet Before Using ☐

2. KICK
   - a. Slow and Easy ☐
   - b. Extended Foot ☐
   - c. Slightly Bent Knee ☐
   - d. Kick From Hips ☐
   - e. No Splash ☐

3. MASK
   - a. Defogging ☐
   - b. Clearing Water Out ☐
   - c. Putting On Under Water ☐
   - d. Equalizing Pressure ☐

4. SNORKEL
   - a. Breathing Properly ☐
   - b. Clearing ☐
   - c. Swimming (No Mask) ☐
   - d. Clear Mask ☐
   - e. Surface Dive ☐

5. MOUTHPIECE UNIT
    a. Swim (No Mask) ☐
    b. Clear Mask ☐
    c. Clear Hoses ☐
    d. Buddy Breathe ☐
    e. Doff and Don ☐

6. FACE MASK UNIT
    a. Swim ☐
    b. Clear Mask ☐
    c. Buddy Breathe ☐
    d. Doff and Don ☐

A Suggested Training Program

Since the development of a series of related skills is best accomplished by progressive learning, the object of this program is to provide the individual or instructor with a guide covering the contents of this manual. The training program as presented is a method of acquiring both theory and skills progressively as they relate to each other.

Instructor techniques, equipment available, prior training, and adaptability will undoubtably alter some of the presentation. However, it should be remembered that short-cutting or lack of knowledge and skill may lead to eventual involvement in panic-inducing situations, for which there is no solution.

Theory presentations accompanying each lesson may be covered by assigned reading, followed by discussion or by instructor's lecture and testing.

Assuming that trainees have no prior knowledge or experience, the following water sessions are designed to be covered in two hours each. Less or more time may be indicated, depending on the trainee's adaptability and the instructor's techniques.

LESSON I—SKIN DIVING (*Assigned Reading: Ch. 5, "Skin Diving Equipment"; Ch. 6, up to "Advanced Skin Diving"; Ch. 3, through "Squeeze"*)

A. Face Mask Skills
    1. Check construction, fit, and seal while dry and then submerged without strap. Adjust strap—recheck for seal and comfort.
    2. Apply fog preventative—saliva or others. Subsequent fogging may be eliminated if a small quantity of water is retained in the mask and used as a rinse when needed. Check visibility.

3. While in a *horizontal position* flood the mask. Clear during 180 degree roll horizontally as described earlier in this chapter. While in *vertical position* flood the mask. Starting with face inclined downward start clearing as described earlier in this chapter. Alter clearing techniques as necessary if "purge valve"-equipped. Sealing the purge valve during initial training may be desirable.

4. Equalizing pressures—mask, ears, sinuses.

B. Snorkel Skills

1. Examine construction. Insert the mouthpiece properly. Breathe through the snorkel above surface. Squat down until mouth and nose are submerged; breathe. Cautious breathing is indicated at first until breathing through the mouth alone is mastered.

2. Squat further down until the snorkel floods. Rise until eyes are above surface. Puff the water out of the tube. Breathe cautiously—some air can be obtained even if some water is still in the "J." Puff again.

3. Attach the snorkel to the mask strap. Adjust so as to remain above water when the face is submerged vertically or horizontally.

4. Breathe with face submerged—mask clear. Flood and clear tube.

5. Breathe with face submerged—mask flooded. Flood and clear tube.

C. Fin Kicks

1. Examine construction. Most types can be worn on either foot but some are specifically labeled right—left. Wet feet and fins; don as described earlier in this chapter. Holding on to poolside or float observe the action as described.

2. Holding to the poolside, face down, perform a slow, moderately wide flutter kick. Adjust as needed. Swim a couple of lengths, with and without armstrokes.

3. Repeat as in above using first the "regular scissors" then the "inverted scissors." Swimming position is turned on the side.

4. Repeat; while holding on in semi-sitting position perform the "bicycle kick" (modified back flutter). Swim a couple of lengths without armstrokes.

5. Hold on in face-down position. Perform the movements of the dolphin kick. Avoid extreme bending at waist or knees. Best initial results are obtained while submerged, so the trial

lengths will necessitate surfacing for breath when needed. After the kick has been mastered, surface adaptations are easily made.

Learning the above leg kicks is generally facilitated if the mask and snorkel are worn. This will permit underwater observation of the instructor and others who may have mastered the kicks. Desirable practice is obtained as all three items of basic equipment are used in learning a skill.

LESSON II—SKIN DIVING (*Assigned Reading: Ch. 6, "Underwater Swimming" and "Submerging" [surface dives], in review; Ch. 2, from "Density and Buoyancy"; Ch. 3, to "Indirect Effects of Pressure"*)

A. Review clearing of flooded mask and snorkel. Retrieve while on bottom in chest-deep water. Practice until both can be cleared in one breath.

B. Using mask, snorkel, and fins, review and practice leg kicks. Introduce mask and snorkel clearing while "snorkeling."

C. Review pressure equalization in mask, ears, sinuses in preparation for surface dives and following underwater activities.

D. Review "hyperventilation"—benefits and precautions—shallow water "blackout." Practice at rest and moving—note time variance.

E. Using the "buddy system" with one up, one down, practice surface dives. IF WEIGHT BELTS ARE NEEDED, this is a good time to introduce them. Determination of needed weight and operation of "quick release" can be combined with hyperventilation and surface dives.

F. Follow up with recovery of mask, snorkel, and fins in deep water. "ONE BREATH RECOVERY" is the goal. Doffing the weight belt after recovery is good practice since this impresses the diver with its emergency value.

G. Practice entries back and front from 1-meter diving board and pool or float side.

H. The latter part of this session may be given over to combining all skills acquired so far. Dependent on the size of the training group, the following exercises to develop thinking and working underwater are suggested for use in entirety or altered as need be:

1. Selecting and fitting washers on a bolt.
2. Tying and untying short lengths of line to a fixed object.
3. Recovering appropriate numbered discs to solve simple math problems. Use an underwater slate and grease pencil for math or communications problems.
4. Setting up an underwater obstacle course and surface floats in such a manner as to exercise skills and thinking.

5. Laying out a grid search for a small clear plastic disk. A limited radial search may also be set up, using a lead block as the pivot point.

NOTE: In all the foregoing Part H, the designated tasks should permit completion without pushing breath-holding to the limit.

LESSON III—SCUBA FAMILIARIZATION (*Assigned Reading: Ch. 4, entirely; Ch. 5, Scuba Equipment; Ch. 6, Use of the Main Types of Scuba*)

Students are formed in buddy teams before preparing and using scuba.

A. Buddy teams select, prepare scuba and related equipment as a predive check. A *checklist* visual aid will help to expedite preparation. If a *cascade system* is available, a demonstration of technique followed by each buddy team filling to prescribed pressure would be advantageous. If filling is done at another location, a trip to the *air station* would be in order before many more lessons are completed.

B. Take all equipment to the shallow end of the pool. Scuba may be carried rather than worn, so as to facilitate use by each trainee. The following exercises will familiarize trainees with demand air flow, "free flow" (in double-hose units), mouthpiece clearing, and hose (double-hose units) clearing by the "puff," "free flow," and purge button" methods. The need for a cautious trial breath rather than the air gulping type common to initiates should be made known before the trainee learns the hard way.

Ridiculous as it may seem, the trainee should be told and impressed with the fact that he must *exhale before* he can expect to *inhale*. Complaints of regulators not functioning, no air, or inability to breathe after mechanically purging the mouthpiece may in many instances be traced to this human failure.

Proper *positioning* of the *single-hose scuba mouthpiece* (exhaust ports *down*) before clearing and breathing will materially aid in this and future exercises.

These initial exercises are designed for both double- and single-hose units. Where difference of technique is indicated, separate coverage will be made.

1. Turn air valve to full open. Note direction of turning. Breathe from mouthpiece (all regulator parts out of water). *Immerse double-hose regulator;* note flow of air from mouthpiece caused by pressure differential between atmosphere and several inches of water. Lower mouthpiece to regulator; flow stops. *Immerse single-hose regulator* (first stage); note that

there is no flow. Pressure difference must occur in the mouth-piece (second-stage demand chamber) before air flow starts. Brief apparent free flow may be noted after a breath is taken in later exercises. Sensitivity or mechanical operation lag may be the cause. Continued unchecked flow indicates malfunction. Locate and press the "purge button" to demonstrate how "free flow" may be mechanically initiated and stopped when desired without raising or lowering the mouthpiece.

2. Submerge with scuba. Flood and clear the mouthpiece by "free flow" or "purge button" methods. Insert the mouthpiece as soon as initial flow has cleared the water. STOP THE FREE FLOW. Exhale into the mouthpiece forcefully (puff); test cautiously to determine if clearing was complete. Breathe if clear. Repeat if necessary and try again.

3. Flood the mouthpiece and clear by forceful exhalation alone (puff method). Check before inhaling fully. Clearing double-hose scuba will be more easily accomplished when using this method if the exhaust hose is lowest.

4. Breathe with mask on and flooded. Clear the mask by both horizontal roll and vertical tilt methods.

C. Station Breathing (three or four scuba anchored at varied distances and depths). This exercise will usually demonstrate some of the difficulties that are initially present when learning to breathe from scuba under other than ideal conditions. Errors in technique may be observed and corrected at this point rather than during more complex doff and don exercises.

NOTE: Special care must be taken in this exercise to prevent unvented ascent after breathing compressed air while submerged. Even in the shallow end of the pool there is potential hazard, and such an ascent could cause some form of barotrauma.

1. Anchor the units in shallow water within easy breath-holding distances. Have trainees (wearing mask and fins) submerge, clear, and take several breaths from each unit in the circuit. Any difficulties can be readily observed and corrected before exercises in deeper water are attempted.

2. Starting at the shallow end, anchor the units progressively to the deepest portion of the pool. Operating as "buddy teams" with one member snorkeling over the submerged member, begin the exercise at No. 1 in the shallow end. Since the progress is downward, breath-holding between the stations pre-

sents no problem. When the last unit is cleared and breathing is satisfactory, have the trainee flood his face mask and cease breathing. Insert snorkel mouthpiece. While ascending along a predetermined 25- to 30-foot sloping line, clear the face mask (this guarantees exhalation during ascent), clear the snorkel, and return to the starting point while snorkeling.

3. Repeat the circuit with a flooded face mask. Clear at the last station and breathe out (maintain an open airway) continually during the sloping ascent. Snorkel to starting point.

D. Examine the scuba harness, the function of each part, its origin at the back pack and the method of adjusting or securing. Make safety hitches where necessary, learn the operation of quick-release buckles or other fastening devices (snaps, EZ hooks, Velcro fasteners) that may be involved in doffing or donning the equipment. Buddy teams don and doff scuba on deck (while sitting is safest). Repeat in chest-deep water. The sitting or kneeling positions can be altered to fit adaptability. Emphasis should be placed on manipulation by feel alone rather than dependence on seeing the parts.

Conclude the lesson with disassembly of scuba ON DECK after turning off the air and breathing the pressure from the regulator as indicated in Chapter 5. Store properly after disassembly and cleaning.

LESSON IV—DOFF AND DON (*Assigned Reading: Ch. 6, "Scuba Doff and Don"; Ch. 2, up to "Density and Buoyancy"; form and solve diving problems after reading*)

A. Teams assemble all gear. Make a predive check of equipment, diver's condition, and after review, the lesson plan to be followed. Review scuba parts (valve, regulator position, reserve lever), harness origin and purpose, function of quick releases. Stress "WEIGHT BELT ON LAST, OFF FIRST" during don and doff.

B. Buddy teams don and doff on bottom in shallow water as a review of technique. Doing this with face mask flooded will increase concentration and encourage feel rather than sight of adjustment of harness.

C. Teams go to deep water—one in scuba, one snorkeling directly over his buddy as safety man. Scuba-equipped diver doffs all equipment (fins may be retained) and ascends while continually exhaling to a surface marker about 25 feet away.

Rest on the surface—THINK—hyperventilate, and dive to the doffed unit. Don as previously practiced. Proceed to shallow water, on bottom and *breathing normally*. Rotate until all have completed the exercise satisfactorily.

NOTE: Again caution novices against unventilated ascent after breathing from scuba. Stress importance of continual observation by safety man and the need for immediate action when a dangerous procedure is observed. Posting the safety man does not relieve the instructor of his responsibility. It serves as a training medium and augments necessary precautions.

LESSON V—BUDDY BREATHING—EXCHANGE—RESCUE (*Assigned Reading: Ch. 3, "Indirect Effects of Pressure" and repetitive dive tables; Ch. 6, "Rescue Skills"; Ch. 7, "Artificial Respiration"*)

A. Predive check equipment and trainees. Outline activity. Warm up with "snorkeling" activities.

B. Buddy breathe in shallow water (weight belts worn if needed) until positions and exchange technique are mastered in both vertical (still) and swimming positions. The description and illustrations in Chapter 6 will serve as a guide. Move to deeper water while swimming and sharing air. Practice moving apart and coming back for a breath.

C. While in deep water rotate scuba equipment to the skin diver as described and illustrated in Chapter 5. (Dependent upon the type of scuba being used, some changes will be necessary or desirable.) Trading the single-hose unit will be easier than the double-hose type and may be accomplished in most any position. Caution must be observed when trading double-hose units so as to avoid the difficulties arising from free flow when the regulator is permitted to be far below the mouthpiece. REMEMBER, EXHALE CONTINUALLY WHILE SURFACING AFTER EXCHANGE.

D. Practice bottom and surface rescue and the tow to a floating base. Determine the most stable position on the type of float used for performing mouth-to-mouth or mouth-to-nose artificial respiration.

LESSON VI—ENTRIES, DARK WATER, AND EMERGENCIES (*Assigned Reading: Ch. 7 entirely; review use of repetitive dive tables; Ch. 9, "Planning a Dive"*)

A. Practice entries while skin and scuba equipped. Prior to this exercise, the usual predive check of equipment and man must be made to simulate actual open-water dives. Failure to harness correctly, turn air on, protect face mask, or position body correctly are less hazardous here than in many possible dive circumstances.

B. This exercise emphasizes the importance of buddy teaming and close observation. The skin-equipped buddy will serve as "safety" even if required to perform some of the following.

1. Scuba diver, with mask window "blacked out" by cardboard inside or nontransparent material secured outside, is disoriented in shallow water by rolling and being somersaulted in the water. He is then headed toward deep water. (While moving, he will keep hands in front and together.) Stop to correct emergencies.

2. The following may be done singly or in combination, preferably by the instructor or knowledgeable assistant:
   a. Remove mouthpiece.
   b. Gradually shut air valve (single-hose units). Clamp either or both hoses (double-hose units). Assist in reaching valve or release hoses when cause of breathing impairment is discovered.
   c. Undo harness buckles or hitches.
   d. Flood the face mask.

Repeat until all emergencies have been experienced and corrected satisfactorily by all.

NOTE: The foregoing is not intended to become a hazing or harassment initiation. Its intent is to test reaction and coordination of response to emergencies. Observation should be critical of panic indication or misjudgment. Primary consideration must be given to the possibility of an unventilated ascent and every precaution taken to prevent it immediately.

LESSON VII—PLANNING THE DIVE—POSSIBLE EMERGENCIES (*Assigned Reading: Ch. 8, "Environment"; general review of all*)

This is a general summation and review of all previously learned skills. Discussion of several planned dive activities and the possible dangers involved will set the stage for exposure to some of the listed miscarriages of planned safety.

A. Predive check: equipment, diver, planned activity. Include the emergency situations and course of corrective action, role of the "safety man."

B. After appropriate entry to fit indicated condition, the designed conditions are encountered and corrected according to plan. Following are suggested situations that can be set up using imagination, experience, and simple props.
   1. Entrapment—net, bag, large plastic trash can, snarled line, etc.
   2. Dark-water loss of safety guide line or buddy line.
   3. Air supply cut off or exhausted—long ascent with no air.

4. Continual flooding of face mask.
5. Loss of one or both fins.
6. Remove scuba; pass through area just big enough to wiggle through; don and continue.
7. Send and receive communications—visual hand signals; written; sound—react accordingly.
8. Buddy breathe with a disabled diver (conscious) to a distant location.
9. Locate and rescue an unconscious diver; with history of the dive reviewed, determine the most likely cause of the diver's condition; act accordingly.
10. Set up and carry out a grid search for a hard-to-find object.
11. Devise methods for lifting a heavy object from the bottom with simple, readily available equipment and materials.
12. Use hand tools underwater to—make a box; assemble pipes. Tie objects together or disassemble objects previously tied.

The relative safety and close observation possible in a pool should be used to every advantage before the open-water checkout is made. Acquirement of skills and knowhow, when emergencies occur, will make the future activities of the diver safe and full of pleasure.

FIG. 47.   SCUBA TO SKIN DIVER EXCHANGE (1)

Skin diver, sitting, grasps cylinder with knees. Scuba diver hands mouthpiece up to skin diver (AIR FLOWS FREELY, SO RESTRICT VOLUME INTAKE). Scuba diver removes weight belt and all harness. Divers "nurse" until both are ready for exchange.

FIG. 48.   SCUBA TO SKIN DIVER EXCHANGE (2)

Scuba diver now moves away from cylinder and harness, weight belt refastened. He begins ascent at 60-feet-per-minute while *exhaling*. Skin diver dons scuba in prescribed manner.

FIG. 49.   SCUBA TO SKIN DIVER EXCHANGE (3)

Surfaced diver now acts as safety. This exercise combines several training techniques. Because of "flooding" air, divers *must* restrict volume intake while nursing (see   Chapter 3, air embolism). Teamwork and care make this an effective exercise.

FIG. 50. NURSE AND TRADE MASKS AT SEVERAL STATIONS

7

FIRST AID FOR DIVING ACCIDENTS

Most diving accidents can be prevented, but even the best-trained diver on the best-run dive can get into real trouble when he least expects it. So it is not enough to know how to "do it right" in the first place. You also have to know what to do if things go wrong. Whether a mishap on one of your dives turns into a full-blown tragedy or not can depend entirely on you or your buddy. There won't be a doctor down there with you to handle medical emergencies, and there may not be a hospital within miles; so you're on your own. If you've had good first aid training and have some emergency plans ready in the back of your head, doing the right thing will be almost automatic. Otherwise, you may be the one who panics and needlessly loses his own life or his buddy's.

Just how important *knowing what to do* is, was shown on a dive made by Jim Stewart and Ron Church, both long-time ace divers from Scripps Institute of Oceanography. They were making scientific observations off Wake Island on March 8, 1961. Suddenly Jim was attacked by a black tip shark and bitten badly on the right arm and elbow. The bite took off muscle down to the bone and even opened the joint. Blood gushed from the severed vessels but Jim applied hand pressure to the brachial artery and stopped the flow. Ron helped him to shore and gave further first aid care. Later, much surgery and weeks of healing were required. The scars are something to see but Jim is back to his valuable work almost as if the attack had not happened. Without this knowledge and presence of mind, he could have bled to death before reaching shore.

Diving alone places the burden of decision, action, and conclusion on the individual. None of us is so self-sufficient that we can exclude a helping hand or the added safety afforded by diving with a competent buddy.

Prevention

This chapter deals with first aid—what to do *after* an accident. Knowing a good deal about that is vital, but remember that the best way to handle any accident is to keep it from happening. Most of the contents of this book are concentrated on just that: PREVENTION. Accident prevention starts primarily with being sure that you're fit for diving and does not stop until you're back on shore after a dive *made* safe by your training in handling yourself underwater and knowing how to plan dives and stay out of trouble. If trouble comes in spite of all the preparations, know how to keep mishaps from becoming accidents. One definition of first aid is, "How to keep an accident from becoming a tragedy."

No one chapter—not even a whole book—could possibly take the place of the hours of training and practice necessary to make a good first aid or lifesaving and water safety man. Although these things take time, it's hard to think of a cheaper form of diver's life insurance. All this chapter can do is serve as a guide to things that divers should know about first aid, a review of the essentials, and a place to look up certain facts (such as care of injuries from marine animals) that can be very important but hard to remember.

General First Aid

Very few serious accidents can be handled entirely without professional medical assistance. However, the fact that such assistance is not immediately at hand hardly ever needs to result in loss of life. A few fairly simple first aid procedures can almost always handle the situation in the meantime. Calmly applying proper first aid on the spot is a far better general rule than madly rushing the victim to the nearest doctor or hospital. This does not mean that there should be any *needless* delay in getting professional help.

Do the Right Thing First

In taking care of the victim of any accident, the first step is to *size up the situation* rapidly but accurately. This will tell you what to do first, and doing the right thing first can be a matter of life or death. Splinting a broken bone is useless if the victim dies within minutes because his breathing has stopped, and artificial respiration won't help a victim who is rapidly bleeding to death. If you have someone to help you, all the really important things can be done almost simultaneously provided you know what *needs* to be done. Ask yourself these questions:

1. *Is he breathing?* If not, artificial respiration takes precedence over absolutely everything *except* the need to control massive bleeding—which you are not likely to miss.
2. *Is he bleeding?* Rapid loss of blood can cause death in so few minutes that it clearly must be controlled at once. Even less obvious bleeding can cause

shock or death in a relatively short time, so it must be discovered and stopped.

3. *Is he in shock?* Shock can and does follow almost any type of injury and can cause death even though the initial injury was unlikely to do so.

If none of these problems which demand immediate attention is found, then proceed to examine the victim as thoroughly as possible so as to find *all* the injuries that he may have sustained. Be extremely gentle and do not move him any more than absolutely necessary in the process of examination or loosening of clothing. Be particularly careful to avoid unnecessary moving of the head and neck. If the neck happens to be broken, such movement can cause death or permanent paralysis. If any broken bone is found or suspected, immobilize the part before moving the victim.

In general, the victim should be kept lying flat with head level with the body, at least until you are sure of the full extent of his injuries. Unless circumstance demands prompt removal to a safer place, do not move him unless you are *sure* it is safe to do so or until he can be moved properly by means of a stretcher or suitable substitute.

In everything that you do, remember that YOUR FIRST DUTY IS NOT TO DO HARM. It is better to do nothing than to do something that makes matters worse. Send for medical help immediately if you can. Never delay getting help while you do things like nonessential bandaging. It is always possible that some condition you may have overlooked, such as internal bleeding or a head injury, demands medical attention urgently.

All these things may seem too obvious and basic to be worth mentioning. Perhaps that is why they are too often forgotten and need emphasis as much as specific first aid procedures.

BLEEDING

Nothing is more urgent than stopping rapid loss of blood, and only artificial respiration is more important than control of even moderate bleeding. Four different methods of control can be employed, either singly or in combination, using materials at hand:

1. *Direct pressure on the wound* either by hand or dressing (sterile or clean cloth in several folds) bandaged in place. It is desirable to use sterile dressings on any wound to reduce the danger of infection. However, serious loss of blood caused by waiting for or transporting to such a dressing may prove far more dangerous than an infection. Bandages should be applied firmly but not tightly enough to hamper circulation.

2. *Hand or finger pressure on the artery* supplying the area of the wound will slow or stop most bleeding from the extremities until a dressing and

bandage are applied. The pressure points located on the inner side of the arm, which cause the brachial artery to be compressed against the arm bone, and pressure points on either side of the groin, which cause the femoral artery to be compressed against the front of the pelvis, are most easily found and most widely used. Others are described in older manuals but have little value, or are difficult to find and hold for any length of time.

3. *Elevation of the affected part* will serve to slow serious bleeding at its onset and during subsequent transport.

4. The TOURNIQUET IS THE LAST RESORT. It must be remembered that when a tourniquet is incorrectly placed venous bleeding is increased and arterial bleeding is unaffected. WHEN A TOURNIQUET IS PLACED CORRECTLY, *several inches above the wound*, the blood supply to the area *below* the constricting band is completely shut off, and the tissues will die from loss of oxygen and food unless surgical attention is obtained within a short time. Contrary to past technique, the tourniquet *should not be loosened* except by the doctor. If, as a last resort, a tourniquet is applied, it should be of flat material about 2 inches wide, tightened till bleeding stops and fixed to continue pressure. The attending physician must be notified that the tourniquet is in place.

SHOCK

All injuries or sudden illnesses are accompanied by some degree of shock. Shock, the slowing down of all body functions, is oftentimes more serious than the injury itself. Therefore, shock care must be initiated as soon as possible. Keeping the victim lying down, quiet, and preserving body heat is reasonably simple and also permits other care at the same time.

STOPPAGE OF BREATHING (ASPHYXIA)

There are many causes for the stopping of breathing associated with diving accidents. Whatever the cause, when breathing has stopped, the victim must be supplied with air by some method. Many methods of artificial respiration (causing an alternate increase and decrease in chest expansion) have been devised and practiced since man recognized the need for such action. Most have succeeded in moving little or no air, although they have on occasion been used successfully.

Very careful and exhaustive research has recently shown that the oldest method of all—inflating the victim by mouth—can be by far the most effective, with no gadgets whatever, provided that the head and neck are placed in the proper position. This method, now called RESCUE BREATHING "mouth-to-mouth or mouth-to-nose" artificial respiration, utilizes the rescuer's exhaled air. The exhaled air has been proved to contain more than enough oxygen to supply the needs of the victim. The rescuer knows positively at every instant whether air is going in and out properly or not, so that if obstruction occurs he will know it at once and take action. A child can successfully ventilate even a large adult, and the method can be used anywhere (even in the water) and under almost all conditions where other methods were difficult, damaging, or impossible.

The sole objection to Rescue Breathing stems from squeamishness, bashfulness, prejudice, and fear of acquiring an infection. Only fear of an infection is an obstacle that intelligent people should be willing to admit, and the actual danger of contracting a serious disease is extremely slight. It should not deter you for one instant from using the method on a fellow diver or any apparently healthy person. When properly done, the method does not involve inhaling the victim's breath. The chance that the victim has a communicable disease or that the rescuer could contract it is remote. Fire, police, and hospital personnel deserve the added protection of mask-and-tube devices that are available. Such devices, in almost every other circumstance, must be condemned because they add nothing to the effectiveness of the procedure and only increase the likelihood of fatal delay in starting or of ineffective application. The possibility of infection is a legitimate objection to frequent or extensive practice of the method, but fortunately most individuals can do it properly after instruction and very limited trial. Manikins for safe and realistic practice are becoming available and will solve the problem of practice.

The following concise description of the method was taken (with minor changes to bring it up to date) from the American Red Cross first aid text (*Supplement on Artificial Respiration*, 4th ed.) along with the accompanying illustrations.

Remove foreign matter from the mouth immediately. If possible, have the victim on a flat surface (do not put anything under the shoulders or let the head hang over an edge). Remember that the head and neck position in relation to the body is essential (Fig. 51, No. 1) and can be achieved properly under any conditions, even when both victim and operator are in the water.

1. By lifting the neck close to the head with one hand while pushing the forehead with the palm of the other, the neck is extended and airway straightened. The above action serves to "jut" the jaw as is shown in Fig. 51, No. 1. The palm so placed on the forehead puts the thumb and forefinger in position to pinch-seal the nose. Alternate straightening and opening of the airway can be achieved by pulling or pushing the lower jaw into a "jutting out" position as in Nos. 2 and 3, Fig. 51.
2. Open your mouth wide and place it tightly over the victim's mouth. At the same time, pinch the nostrils shut (4) or close the nostrils with your

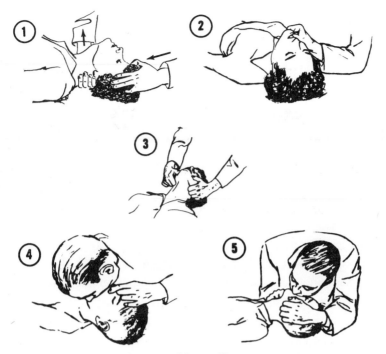

FIG. 51. MOUTH-TO-MOUTH RESUSCITATION

(Figs. 51 and 52 used by courtesy of the American Red Cross)

cheek (5), or close the victim's mouth and place your mouth over the nose. Blow into the mouth, or nose. (Air can be blown through the victim's teeth even though they are clenched.) *The first blowing efforts should determine whether or not obstructions exist.*

3. Remove your mouth, turn your head to the side and listen for the return rush of air that indicates air exchange. Repeat the blowing effort.

  For an adult, blow vigorously at the rate of about 12 breaths per minute.

  For a child, take relatively shallow breaths appropriate for the child's size, and puff the air in by cheek action at the rate of about 20 per minute.

4. If air exchange is not free and easy, recheck head and neck position and try pulling jaw forward. If still obstructed, foreign material may be present. Recheck the mouth. Try brisk pressure just above margin of the ribs immediately after attempting inflation and see if this moves particles or secretions up to the mouth. If not, turn the victim on his side and administer sharp blows between the shoulder blades (Fig. 52, No. 7). If continued presence of secretions or vomitus is a problem, keep victim on side to permit drainage. Be careful to maintain proper head position. Lean over the victim from behind to continue mouth inflation.

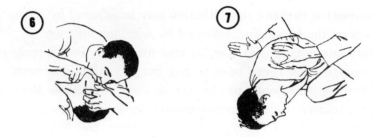

Fig. 52. Jaw Held Forward by Finger in Mouth (6) and Attempt to
Dislodge Obstruction (7)

Every diver should be familiar with Rescue Breathing and should, if possible, practice applying it under different circumstances. In the water, the best situation is to have the operator supported by a float and able to hold the victim's neck and head. If only one hand is free, a hold at the chin may be effective. There is no harm in letting the victim's head submerge during the inflation phase (nose and mouth are sealed). REMEMBER THE VITAL IMPORTANCE OF THE HEAD BACK–NECK FORWARD POSITION. It is critical in an unconscious victim, while almost any position will work on a conscious volunteer "victim."

No other method of artificial respiration is discussed or shown here, since it is difficult to justify instruction in or any continued recognition of the older procedures.

The victim should be observed closely after revival and kept quiet, lying down, and body heat preserved (blankets under and over). By all means obtain the services of a physician as soon as possible.

STOPPAGE OF THE HEART (CARDIAC ARREST)

Until very recently, cessation of heart action (a very frequent consequence of drowning and other forms of aphyxia, of electrocution, and of heart attacks) could be handled only by opening the chest and pumping the heart by hand. This clearly was a job for the physician and, since it must be done immediately, was of little use in the field. Now there is an extremely effective procedure for pumping the heart by applying pressure to the chest from the outside. Full description of the method is beyond the scope of this chapter. Briefly however, the following will give some idea of the mechanics:

The victim is placed face up on a hard, flat surface. The operator kneels, places the heel of his right hand on the center of the victim's chest, then places his left hand on his right hand. Pressure is then applied downward, compressing the rib cage about 1 inch. The release of pressure is sudden. This pressure and release is repeated about 60 to 80 times per minute.

A second operator performs Rescue Breathing (mouth-to-mouth or mouth-to-nose) at the same time. Rhythm may be adjusted by giving four to five strokes on the breastbone, followed by one lung inflation.

If only one rescuer is present, he may manage by interrupting external cardiac massage every thirty beats to give five or six lung inflations.

Medical assistance must be obtained as soon as possible. More detailed information relative to cardio-pulmonary (heart-lung) resuscitation may be obtained by ordering CG 139, April, 1963, from the Superintendent of Documents, U.S. Government Printing Office, Washington, D.C. 20402 (20 cents).

Since this is a vital and intricate phase of first aid, detailed knowledge of procedure, cause, and effect is the responsibility of all who would attempt it.

WOUND CARE

Aside from bleeding control, which has been discussed, here are a few general directions for the care of wounds. Following these will greatly reduce the chance of infection and add to the comfort of the victim, as well as making the later medical attention less complicated.

1. Whenever giving first aid care to any opening in the skin the first-aider should have clean hands.
2. Soap and clean water (preferably boiled) may be used to cleanse the area. Care must be exercised to prevent dirt or foreign material from entering the wound.
3. If the wound will receive further care by a physician, it is best that no antiseptic be applied. Consult your doctor concerning antiseptics to be be placed in first aid kits.
4. Cover the wound with a sterile dressing, and bandage in place snugly but not so tightly that circulation is impaired.
5. Even in minor wounds, if signs of infection appear (redness, swelling, pus) bring them to the attention of a physician.

PREVENTION OF TETANUS

Tetanus (lockjaw) is a commonly fatal disease caused by germs found in soil, dirt, mud, etc. These germs enter the body through a break in the skin. Minor wounds, particularly punctures, can be dangerous if sustained where contamination is at all likely; they demand that the victim be protected against the disease. This is certainly true of divers injured in mud or dirty water. There are two methods of protection: use of *tetanus antitoxin*, which requires several injections at the time of injury and can cause troublesome reactions; and the use of *tetanus toxoid*, which seldom causes any difficulty. Tetanus toxoid is given as a routine immunization, and most people have had it either as children or as members of the armed forces. If the individual has received a "booster" *within three years*, all that needs to be given at the time of injury is a small additional dose. *Unfortunately*, very few adults have kept their boosters "up to date" and, if injured, must receive the antitoxin instead. Very few divers are aware of the danger of tetanus in underwater injuries. A sensible diver will get the protection of tetanus toxoid immunization and will apply for the additional dose if he is injured under dirty conditions on land or in water.

Since much diving water is contaminated to some degree, divers are also unusually exposed to all waterborne diseases, including polio. It therefore makes good "safe diving sense" to see your doctor and make sure that all your immunizations (which everyone should have anyhow) are up to date.

FRACTURES

First aid for fractured bones consists mainly of careful handling (or no handling, unless necessary) so as not to increase the injury. If the victim must be moved or transported other than in an ambulance under expert supervision, the fracture should be immobilized. Using whatever *suitable* materials are at hand (appropriate length, weight, and strength) for splints; apply these in such a manner as to keep the broken bone ends from moving and at the same time prevent movement of the adjacent joints. Careful transportation and treatment of shock are essential.

BURNS

First aid for burns is dependent on the degree and the amount of area involved. Burns are classified as:

> *First Degree*—reddening of the skin
> *Second Degree*—blisters
> *Third Degree*—charring or deep destruction of tissues

Pain can be relieved by exclusion of air through the application of many-layered sterile dressings (dry) and bandaging in place. Small areas of first or second degree may be well cared for by the careful application of medically approved preparations and sterile dressings.

The commonest type of burn suffered by divers is sunburn. Long exposure, both in and out of water, has taken all the pleasure out of many a well-planned and -executed diving trip. Gradual tanning may be accomplished by initial short exposure time, increased daily until the desired protective pigment layer is built up. Shielding the skin with light clothing, or in some instances the application of shielding lotions or creams, will prevent painful or even serious burns.

Shock care is imperative when large areas of any degree are involved and shock is generally a threat even where relatively small areas have suffered third-degree burns. Since infection and other complications might be involved, the attention of a physician should be sought.

First Aid for Diver Affected by Chilling

Symptoms are mentioned in Chapter 3 as well as the warning to avoid being so affected. Loosing tactile sense, uncontrollable shivering, and paralysis may well be classed as injuries of serious nature.

The indicated first aid care is prompt removal from the water to an adequate outside heat source such as a bonfire or a heated enclosure. Merely wrapping in blankets or drinking hot liquids will not suffice.

Prevention is as important as care. Wear adequate insulating clothing and don't ignore the primary warnings. Get out while you are able.

First Aid Kit

A simple metal or well-constructed box of some moistureproof material to contain first aid materials should be standard equipment on every dive. The following items are suggested in the American Red Cross 16-unit kit:

Two 1-inch adhesive compresses
One 2-inch bandage compress
One 3-inch bandage compress
One 4-inch bandage compress
One package 3″ × 3″ plain gauze
    pads
One 2-inch gauze roller bandage
One tube burn ointment

Two plain absorbent gauze
    ½ sq. yd.
Two plain absorbent gauze
    24″ × 72″
Three triangular bandages
One scissors, tweezers, and 6 inches
    of ½-inch dowel to be used as
    the windlass when applying a
    tourniquet

Supplementary items desirable in the first aid care of marine life injuries would include:

Baking soda
Nonprescription ointment for relief
    of pain (applied locally)

Antihistamine tablets
Antihistamine ointment

Read and follow directions for dosage or application of any drugs included in the kit.

Injuries From Marine Life Contact

It would be virtually impossible to cover all the injuries possible and their care in a manual such as this. Many books, research papers, and technical reports available are the product of patient, trying, and costly experiments and research compiled by scientists, professional divers, and amateurs.

The following information is a general coverage for first aid which may be administered by the diver with subsequent attention by a physician:

Cause	Prevention	Symptoms	First Aid
Marine Plants	Avoid fast, entangling movements.		Move straight up to surface. Look for clear spot. Drop straight down and swim to clear area. Repeat till clear of plant bed.
Coral	Wear shoes, gloves protective clothing around coral. Avoid contact, be especially careful of surge effects toward coral heads.	Cuts, abrasions, welts, pain, and itching. Severe reactions are not usual.	Rinse area with baking soda solution, weak ammonia, or plain water. Apply cortisone or antihistamine ointment. Antihistamine may be given by mouth to reduce initial pain and reaction. When initial pain subsides, cleanse the area with soap and water, apply an antiseptic, and cover with sterile dressings. Severe cases or those not responding readily should be referred to a physician.
Sea Urchin	Avoid contact. Spines will penetrate most forms of protective covering.	Often immediate and intense burning sensation followed by redness, swelling, and aching. Weakness, loss of body sensation, facial swelling, and irregular pulse may be noted. Severe cases involving paralysis, respiratory distress, and even death have been noted.	Remove as many spines as possible with forceps (tweezers, pliers). Cleanse the area and cushion with large, loose dressings. If signs of infection appear, seek medical attention promptly.
Cone Shells	Avoid contact with soft parts of the animal.	Puncture wound. Reduction of blood supply (cyanosis). Stinging, burning sensation at first. Numbness, abnormal sensation begins at wound and spreads rapidly. In severe cases: paralysis, respiratory distress, coma, heart failure.	No specific care. Remove from water immediately. Keep lying down. Get medical attention as soon as possible. See section on first aid for venomous fish sting (general).
Jelly Fish (Coelenterates), Sea Nettles, Portuguese Man-of-War, Sea Wasp	Be alert—avoid contact. Wear protective clothing when present, also on night dives. Avoid whole or partial "dead" parts either in or out of water.	Variable, according to species. Vary from mild stinging to intense burning, throbbing, or shooting pain; may be accompanied by unconsciousness, reddened skin, welts, blisters, swelling, skin hemorrhage. In some cases, shock, cramps, loss of tactile senses, vomiting, paralysis, respiratory difficulty and convulsions, and death. The SEA WASP has caused death within several minutes.	Obtain buddy assistance and leave water. Remove tentacles and as much of stinging material as possible with cloth, seaweed, or sand. Avoid spreading. Apply weak ammonia solution saturated solution of baking soda in water or fresh clean water. Apply cortisone or antihistamine ointment. Anesthetic ointment to relieve pain. Obtain medical attention as soon as possible in severe cases. If the Portuguese Man-of-War or Sea Wasp is the cause, medical help is essential.

Cause	Prevention	Symptoms	First Aid
Octopus	Avoid being trapped by tentacles. Porous clothing will hinder action of cups. To prevent bite, avoid mouth area at tentacle origin.	Beak bites (two) produce stinging, swelling, redness, and heat. Bleeding out of proportion to size of wound.	Apply cold compresses. Keep lying down, feet elevated. Get medical attention as soon as possible if bitten. No specific care other than bleeding control if profuse.
Sting Rays	Avoid stepping on in shallow water. Shuffle fins to scare away. Avoid contact with barb at base of tail.	Pain within 4 to 10 minutes. Fainting and weakness. Pain increases and may affect entire limb within 30 minutes. Pain maximum in 90 minutes. Wound may be of puncture or laceration type.	Remove from water immediately. Wash with sterile saline solution or cold, clean water. Remove remaining portions of barb sheath. Soak in plain hot water for 30 minutes. Hot compresses may be used if soak is not practical. Get medical attention promptly if wound is in chest or abdomen or if symptoms do not subside with heat application.
Venomous Fish: Horned Sharks, Catfish, Weeverfish, Scorpion Fish, Rabbit Fish, Ratfish, Toadfish, Zebra Fish, Surgeonfish, Stonefish	When diving in unfamiliar areas, consult local divers or appropriate information source regarding existing harmful marine life native to the area.	Variable with type and contact. Usually of puncture type but may be lacerations. Poison introduced by spines causes redness, swelling, pain, general malaise, muscle spasms, respiratory distress with convulsions, and death in severe cases.	Three objectives of care are to: (1) alleviate pain, (2) combat effects of venom, (3) prevent secondary infection. Remove from water immediately. Irrigate with clean, cold water. Make small incision across the wound, apply suction. Soak in water as hot as can be tolerated (without scalding) for 30 to 60 minutes. Epsom salts added to water may be beneficial. Further cleansing should be done after soaking. Obtain medical aid as soon as possible. Ice-water treatment has not been included because of impracticality at average divesite.
Bite Wounds: Shark, Barracuda, Moray Eel, Orca, others	Avoid attracting the predators. Swim quietly while surveying the underwater area. Avoid wearing shiny equipment or sun reflecting on face plate when predators are near. The best prevention is to get out of the water when possibly harmful fish are present.	Serious lacerations from curved bite of shark, straight bite of barracuda, and jagged combination of puncture and laceration by moray eel usually cause severe bleeding, loss of tissue, and extreme shock.	Control serious bleeding by whatever method or methods are possible, immediately. Remove from water immediately. Treat shock and get medical (surgical) aid as soon as possible. Remember loss of blood can be deadly in a short time, and only immediate control can prevent death.

Cause	Prevention	Symptoms	First Aid
Sea Snakes	Avoid handling or contact with netted specimens. Their reported docile nature may be overrated.	Little local sign at bite area. Toxic signs appear within 20 minutes after bite. Malaise, anxiety, euphoria, muscle spasm, respiratory distress, convulsions, unconsciousness, all signs of shock. Mortality rate, 25 per cent.	Leave water immediately. Place restricting band above the bite so as to slow the venous flow to the heart. *This is not a tourniquet.* Loosen every 30 minutes. Keep victim at complete rest. Get medical aid quickly. If possible, identify the snake (IT MAY NOT BE A POISONOUS TYPE).
Inedible poisonous marine animals (too numerous and variable to list)	Consult local divers, fishermen, state or federal bulletins if planning to dive, spear fish, in unfamiliar area. Seafood edible in one area may be poisonous in another.	Variable. Usually start with tingling about lips and tongue, spreading to extremities. Nausea, vomiting, diarrhea, and thirst are common. Muscular incoordination, numbness, paralysis, and convulsions are not uncommon. Symptoms may occur any time within 30 hours after eating the fish.	Empty the stomach as soon as possible. Large amounts of water (5 or 6 glasses), warm and with salt added, should be swallowed. A touch of the finger on the palate will then usually bring up the stomach contents. More water will aid in cleansing the intestinal tract. If rash or welts appear, and the victim is able, cool showers may give some relief. If poisoning is due to eating clams or mussels, baking soda added to the water is beneficial. Obtain the services of a doctor. Save a small quantity of the fish for analysis and possible aid to medication in severe cases.

Injuries From Pressure

Air embolism, decompression sickness, nitrogen narcosis, squeeze, and the effects of oxygen, carbon dioxide, and carbon monoxide when breathed at higher than normal partial pressures have all been discussed thoroughly in other chapters. Cause, symptoms, and prevention are (or should be) so impressed on the trainee and the experienced diver that there would rarely be occasion to employ the first aid methods suggested. Little can be done as a first aid measure in the first two, since recompression in a recompression chamber under trained medical supervision is mandatory. Elsewhere (Chapter 3) in this book are tables of treatment and preventive measures, so there is no need for repetition here. Nitrogen narcosis (if recognized as existing) requires the simplest of all first aid—simply ascend until the effects disappear.

The remainder of the effects mentioned above usually bring about physical injury, asphyxia, unconsciousness akin to severe shock, or a combination of symptoms described in any standard first aid course. This chapter has dealt with the most common symptoms and should act only as a guide to procedure. More detailed procedures are learned in standard and advance Red Cross first aid courses, which should be attended by every safety-minded diver. A good first aid manual should also be in the first aid kit as a vital item of equipment on every dive. Learn and practice the techniques of first aid; they will promote your safety consciousness.

Ten Commandments for Safe Diving

1. BE FIT. Have a medical checkup. Be a good swimmer. Exercise regularly. Don't dive if you feel below par.
2. GET GOOD TRAINING. Reading a book is not enough; enroll in a good course. Learn the facts and *procedures* of safe diving.
3. HAVE GOOD EQUIPMENT. Be careful about "bargains" and don't "build it yourself." Keep your equipment in top condition; check it before every dive.
4. NEVER DIVE ALONE. Always have a "buddy" with you underwater. Have a tender at the surface whenever possible.
5. KNOW THE DIVING AREA. Avoid dangerous places and poor conditions. Take whatever special precautions the area requires.
6. USE A BOAT, FLOAT, OR BOTH. FLY THE DIVER'S FLAG. Be able to reach safety fast. If motorboats are in the area, surface only close to your diver's flag and *with caution.*
7. PLAN YOUR DIVE. Solve the problems in advance. Know decompression rules. Keep track of depth and time. Stick to your plans.
8. BE READY FOR EMERGENCIES. Have plans of action ready. Know lifesaving, first aid, and rescue breathing. Have first aid equipment. Have a diver's I.D. card.
9. BEWARE OF BREATH-HOLDING. *With scuba:* breathe continuously throughout the dive; EXHALE *all the way up on an emergency ascent. Without scuba:* avoid excessive "overbreathing" before skin dives; don't overexert; *don't push your limit on breath-holding.*
10. GET MEDICAL ATTENTION if any abnormality develops during or after a dive. Don't waste time; don't try to "drown the problem." Wear your I.D. card after any dive that might cause "bends."

E. H. LANPHIER, M.D.

Bibliography

U.S. Navy Diving Manual, NAVSHIPS 250-538.
Dangerous Marine Animals, Bruce W. Halstead, M.D. Cambridge, Md.: Cornell Maritime Press.

Skin Diver Magazine, P.O. Box 111, 11200 Long Beach Blvd., Lynwood, Cal., June, 1961.

American National Red Cross First Aid Manual and *Artificial Respiration Supplement*

Spectrum (New York: Pfizer Laboratories), July, 1960 (Vol. 8 No. 7).

Reader's Digest, November, 1960 (article from "Today's Health" in the *American Medical Association Journal*).

8

ENVIRONMENT AND MARINE LIFE

Since approximately three quarters of the earth's surface is covered by water, both fresh and salt, there is a body of water close to every potential diver. So many surface and underwater conditions are present in the waters of the earth that the world-traveling diver is presented with a myriad of problems, each with its individual treatment. Personal experience and the knowledge gained from scientific studies of others has amassed a huge store of knowhow. Drawing from this storehouse of knowledge we can establish generalized procedures and safe diving practices for the new or even the experienced diver.

There are many problems confronting the diver, such as climate, temperature variations, surface and underwater movements, visibility, shore and bottom contours, and marine life. The generalization of the preceding problems, their importance to the diver, and recommend procedures to be followed in safe diving practice is the purpose of the following discourse.

Climate

Until a few years ago, climate limited swimming and diving activities to a few months in temperate zones and, except for the most rugged, confined water activities, to the bathtub in the extreme north and south of these zones. Only in tropical and near-tropical climates could human beings enjoy year-round water activity.

Thanks to the demands of growing numbers of skin and scuba divers all over the globe for protective clothing in the form of wet or dry rubber suits these seasonal limitations are being erased. Choice of such clothing should be governed by existing temperature variations, both climatic and those due to changes at depths. Manufacturers' specifications and the section on "Temperature" in Chapter 2 will help you to determine proper type.

Various climate areas also greatly affect the variety of marine life encountered by the undersea diver, as you will see later.

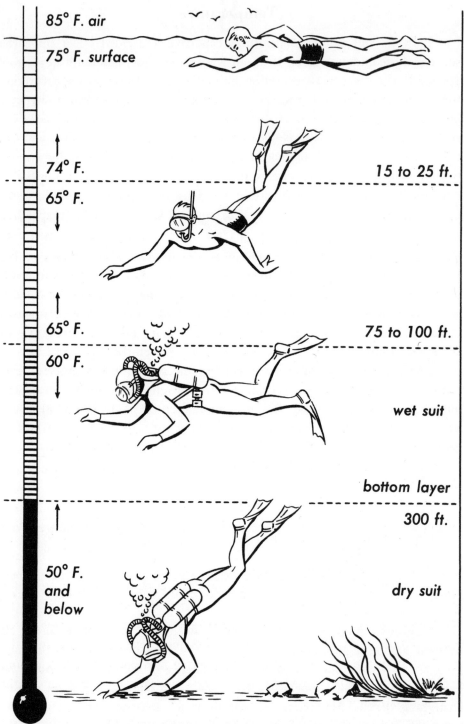

85° F. air

75° F. surface

74° F.   15 to 25 ft.

65° F.

65° F.   75 to 100 ft.

60° F.

wet suit

bottom layer

300 ft.

50° F.
and
below   dry suit

FIG. 53. THERMOCLINES

Temperatures and depths vary with the area, and those given here are for illustration only.

Temperature

Both air and water temperatures can have a decided effect upon the success of the undersea diver. If the air is warm (or hot) and the water is cool (or cold) the diver must condition himself to this transition upon entering the water. The diver (skin or scuba) should, if water temperature warrants, be wearing insulating apparel so as to more nearly eliminate this need for transition. However, if this is not the case, let us consider what does and can happen. First, the shock of radical change brings on quick, gasping inspiration of air and tensing of muscles, making normal activity nearly impossible until the nervous system acclimates itself. This initial response to cold water can be lessened by gradual entry (prolongation of agony). Comparative safety is assured by the proximity of terra firma (more firma and less terra) in the event more drastic reactions, such as numbness or cramps, occur. Having waited out the initial effects of cold the scuba diver can then insert the mouthpiece or don full-face mask of the unit and *cautiously* begin activities. To enter such water while breathing from his tank supply means cutting down his diving time considerably due to his rapid breathing in adjusting to the cold.

Continued loss of body heat in cold water can and will produce in time some serious effects, such as muscle cramps, progressive immobility, insensibility to pain, and complete slowing down of body and mental functions. With this in mind, the wise diver will beware of varying temperatures at depths. These temperature variations (thermoclines) are often dramatic, and they vary from time to time depending on depth, current, season, and weather conditions. For example: many lakes and quarries are quite comfortable for surface swimming, but upon diving to depths of 15 to 20 feet (variable) one encounters extremely cold water. Similar temperature levels are found to exist in nearly all bodies of water, and must be considered in planning a safe underwater trip.

We conclude from the foregoing that insulation against heat loss must be adequate to protect against temperatures encountered, and exit from the water to some heat source must be made before chilling takes place. Even with maximum insulation this chilling takes place eventually and must be anticipated by the safe diver. Plan ahead, taking into account surface action, currents, and possible marine life encounters so that you won't be caught short by your limitations.

Contrary to land conditions, water temperature is fairly uniform, and the entire range is from 28.5° F. in the arctic to 85° F. in some tropical areas. Three quarters of the sea's surface has a seasonal change of less than 9° F.

Surface Action

The many types of surface action are of prime importance to the diver because of their effect on his entry, exit, and surface swimming and their indication of what lies beneath the surface.

Wave action may vary from the gentle shore-lapping type in protected waters to the violent, smashing breakers of a stormy sea. Usually ocean beach waves give indications of depth and bottom contour to the careful observer.

even—shallow

FIG. 54. NO BAR OR REEF OFFSHORE

Waves breaking out from the beach and pushing up to the shore as a welling flood indicate a gradual slope and fairly even bottom. The height of the waves from break to trough will give a rough estimate of the depth from trough to the bottom.

Waves breaking offshore then rolling in and breaking again indicate a reef, sand bar, or some sizable obstruction in the area of the first break.

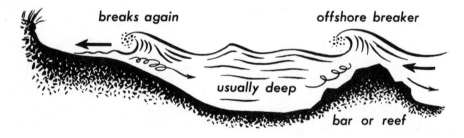

breaks again   offshore breaker

usually deep

bar or reef

FIG. 55. BAR OR REEF OFFSHORE

The frequency of (or interval between) waves breaking on the shore or reef, and their pattern, is usually fairly constant, and after watching for a while the diver can determine where and in what manner to enter or exit safely. Wait till the larger wave breaks and quickly follow the back-surge out, diving under the next smaller ones and continuing outward underwater past the line of breakers. Wait until quieter and deeper water is reached before engaging in diving operations.

When heavy surf is running because of storm, strong currents, or under-sea disturbances, it is wisest to postpone activities until the conditions are safer. Heavy surf can make entry and exit extremely hazardous even if attempted without operational equipment or float. Such equipment as floats, spears, arbaletes, lengths of line, nets, and abalone irons when tossed about by a breaking wave become dangerous missiles. Masks are ripped across the face, and fins worn in surf are an invitation to unpleasant weeks in a plaster cast. When entering through surf, equipment is trailed *behind the diver* by means of a hand line. Several divers entering should do so at separated points and assemble beyond the breaker line in calmer water.

FIG. 56.   UNDER THE BREAKERS, TOWING A FLOAT

Exit from surf along the beach should be accomplished by watching the pattern and going in behind a smaller wave (flippers in hand) and making a quick run to the beach before the big one slips up on you. The float with all equipment lashed securely should be pushed in *ahead* of you and the tow line held in hand.

Entry from a rocky shore should be made at a point where the sea surges up without dashing in a welter of spray and drops back from the rocks smoothly. Observe the wave action in the vicinity of your choice of entry. Breaking waves or upsurgings will indicate the presence of underwater obstructions. Wait until you know the pattern, then wait for the highest surge and enter quickly by jumping or simply falling in; *don't dive.* Swim down and away before the next in-surge. Keep an arm extended as protection from unseen obstacles.

Exit to a rocky shore should be made at a similar point. Remove fins and hold in one hand leaving the feet and one hand free to climb quickly to safety before the next in-surge.

Before entering from unknown beaches or rocky shores try to learn as much about the area conditions from local divers and Coast and Geodetic Survey information as possible.

Currents

Currents affect the distribution of small marine life and change temperatures. Whether caused by tide, wind, or the earth's rotation, these currents tend to move toward the right, or clockwise, in the northern hemisphere and counterclockwise in the southern hemisphere. The most regular are the Japan current of the Pacific and the Gulf Stream of the Atlantic.

The Gulf Stream is a mile deep and averages ninety-five miles wide, flowing at about three knots. This warm current is responsible for normally tropical fish appearing far north during the summer, also for reefs and tropical fish in the temperate zone of Florida.

Currents in the Pacific carry warm surface waters out to sea, and the cold waters of the depths rise to replace them, thus making the waters of the Pacific Coast of the United States colder in summer than those of the east coast.

Tidal currents are of more concern to the diver than these broad rivers of the sea, and they rate a close look.

Tides and their resultant current changes must be considered in all safe diving activities. Since these tidal cycles occur at different times and more or less frequently in various parts of the world, the wise diver will obtain tide tables for the area to be visited.

Currents which move parallel to the shore will change direction completely with the tide and increase or decrease in intensity as the tide wanes or runs in flood. The unwary diver may find himself far from his entry point, or his float many yards away unless it is anchored or secured to the person. Remember, a diver's speed even with flippers will average less than one knot, so trying to gain distance against a one-knot current will be an exhausting, useless effort. Work with the current, angling in or out as desired, keeping in mind that a long walk is a lot safer than an exhausting swim. These tidal currents are regular in specific locations and easily determined by consulting published tide tables, but others are present which must be discovered or learned of before entering an unfamiliar area.

Local peculiarities in current caused by jetties, coves, prominences, reefs, and sand bars are ever present, and necessitate some careful planning of entry, activity, and exit *before* they are encountered rather than when their presence becomes painfully obvious. The accompanying sketches will probably make these situations clearer than could words. Study them carefully.

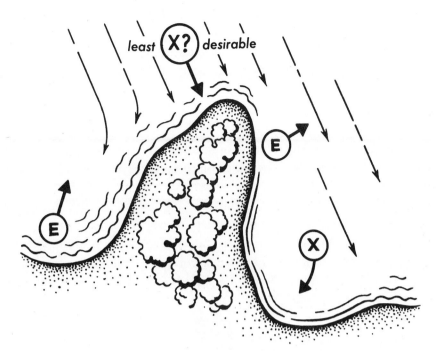

FIG. 57. POINTS

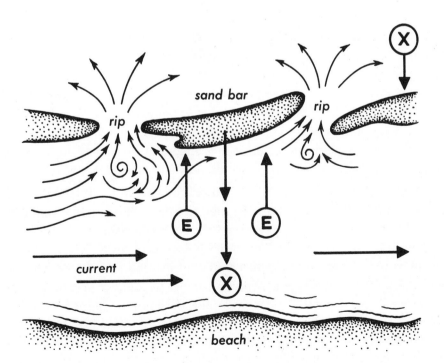

FIG. 58. RIP CURRENTS

When entry is assisted by currents, the skin diver will find he has more energy conserved for the sport at hand; and the scuba diver will find that air is saved for longer dives. Planned, easy exit is made in the same way.

Perhaps one of the greatest contributing causes to drownings and swimmers in trouble off ocean beaches is the "rip current." This particular type of current is caused by water flowing seaward through a gap in a bar or reef, setting up a swirling inshore leading into a strong current outward which carries the unwary or uninitiated rapidly away from the safety of shallow water. Experienced divers quite often utilize these "rips" as an easy, fast road out beyond the reef or bar.

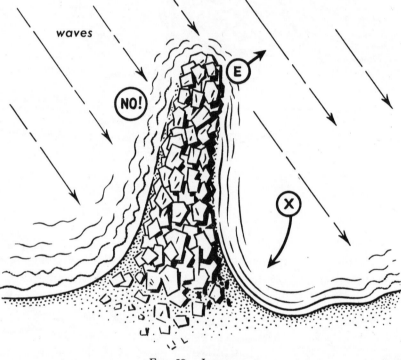

Fig. 59. Jetties

The "rip" can usually be recognized by watching for a gap in the continuous line of "breakers" over a reef. Closer in shore considerable turbulence may be noted in the area of the "rip," accompanied by an interruption of the pattern of waves breaking near the shore.

Fortunately the "rip current" continues beyond the reef or bar only a short distance, then splits and disperses parallel to the reef or bar. If you are caught unaware, relax, ride it out, and return leisurely, with the waves well to either side of the "rip."

Currents, regardless of cause or location, also carry silt, minute marine life, and debris, all of which tend to reduce visibility in varying degrees, depending on their concentration.

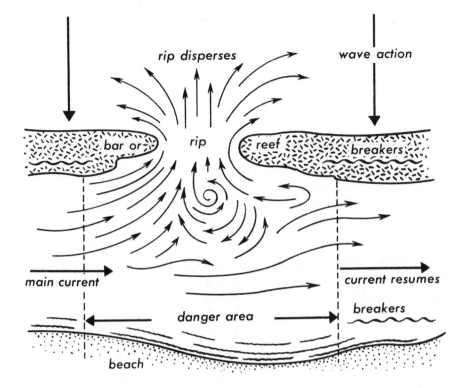

FIG. 60. PATTERN OF RIP CURRENT

Visibility

Graduation from the inadequate naked eye to the all-revealing face mask made visibility an important factor to newcomers in the undersea world. Where visibility at its best was previously only a few hazy feet, now many can see as far as water conditions permit. Open water and silt-free lakes and streams are many times as clear as glass but become almost as dark as a clothes closet when currents or streams stir up or carry in small particles which bar penetration of light. Harbors, rivers, estuaries, and open water in their vicinity are often near zero in visibility ranges and not conducive to safe diving. Often these murky waters carry products of pollution which could be injurious to the diver. Sharp and jagged metal or glass, old pilings, rocks, and long-abandoned, sunken hulks endanger skin and equipment. If circumstances demand diving in water of poor visibility, extreme caution before, during, and after diving should be the order of the day. Guide lines should be used in area searches. Buddies should be connected by a length of line. Waterproof lights should be used. A lookout topside with boat or float to keep surface craft clear is a safety must. A good first aid kit, ear rinse, and shower facilities should be nearby. It is better to travel a little farther to clear water than to risk injury or infection in dirty, dark waters. Even open water can be dangerous when visibility is poor. Remember there are others in the sea who may mistake you for a choice dinner or an undesirable companion, or may inflict injury merely because you unwittingly touched their protective mechanisms.

Entering the Water

Surf beach, sandy bottom. After a predive check of all equipment to be sure that it is workable, approach the chosen takeoff spot. Put on plate, fins, and gloves. Wait for a calm spell between "sets" of waves and wade out. If using a float, you can lie with the upper portion of your body on the float and kick your way beyond the breaker line. Once clear of the breaker line, you will be in calm water. If caught by breaking waves, either hang tightly to the float or, if the breaker is very large, you may find it necessary to dive beneath the surface. In this case you will lose your float and will have to return for it. It may be necessary also to get rid of the spear to prevent injury. Usually this can be avoided by properly timing the calm spells and swimming rapidly until beyond the breaker line.

Surf beach, rocky bottom. Time the waves and swells. Try to pick a spot where the water gets deep quickly. When walking over rocks remember that seaweed and moss are very slippery. Proceed with caution. Get afloat as soon as possible and swim rapidly until in the clear. It is advisable to have the face plate in position before starting, so that you can look ahead underwater to avoid any shallow rocks or masses of weed. A straight-knee kick should be used for propulsion until in deep water to avoid striking the knees or legs on rocks. When going through breaking waves it is wise to hold face mask to face with one hand to prevent its being torn free and lost.

Diving in the Ocean

Many desirable ocean diving areas are characterized by floating and underwater weed, rocky holes, and crevices. The nature of the environment is such that surface and underwater surges occur regularly. The diver should use these water movements to his advantage. Only actual experience in this type of diving will build a knowledge of what happens and how to use it to your advantage. If possible, you should go in company with an experienced ocean diver who can instruct you. In general, the diver can be cautioned to avoid entering deeply into underwater caves and crevices, particularly if surge is heavy. Avoid, also, sudden movements if partially wrapped in weed moved by an underwater surge. In a few seconds the surge will reverse itself, and the weed will move away. It is not likely that you will be seriously entangled while swimming and diving around kelp without scuba. Always look up when coming to the surface to avoid coming up under a rock, a boat, a game-filled sack, another diver, or a matted mass of floating kelp. Return to the beach before fatigued or chilled.

RETURNING THROUGH SURF OVER SAND BOTTOM

Again, time the surf and come in during a flat spell. If caught by a large wave it is usually satisfactory to hang tightly to the tube or float since you will be washed in the direction you wish to go. You may want to drop the spear to avoid possible injury. In general, currents in the center of a cove

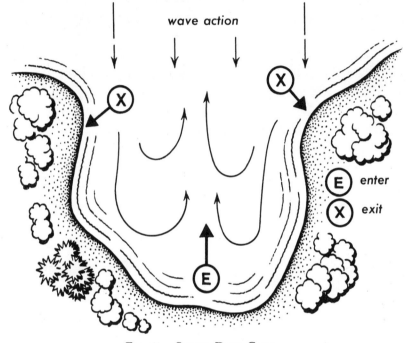

FIG. 61. SMALL DEEP COVE

travel outward while those at the edge travel inward. This fact can be used to your advantage. As soon as you can progress more quickly by wading rather than swimming, get to your feet and wade rapidly to the beach.

RETURNING THROUGH SURF, ROCKY BOTTOM

Due to tidal changes, it may be desirable to return at a different spot from the entry point. Before starting in to the beach, study the situation for a short time. When return point is determined, attempt to make shore during a calm spell. SWIM ALL THE WAY TO THE BEACH IF POSSIBLE. This will avoid stumbling and staggering over the uneven bottom. If caught by a very large wave, let the tube go, submerge, and grab a double handful of kelp to avoid being "rolled" against the rocks. When turbulence has passed, surface and continue. It may be necessary to repeat this procedure.

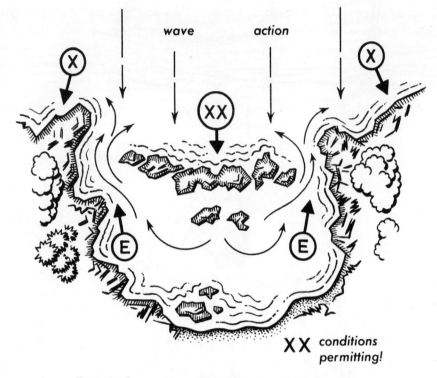

FIG. 62.   ROCKY COVE WITH ROCKS OR REEF OFFSHORE

Diving in Fresh Water

Generally speaking, few unusual problems are encountered when diving in quiet fresh water. However, some points should be considered:

Buoyancy. The swimmer is less buoyant in fresh water. This may not affect a person who habitually swims in this element. However, it may make necessary additional practice in floating or in resting in a floating position. A salt water diver entering fresh water must be alert to differences in buoyancy.

Underwater obstacles. Fallen trees, underwater snags, luxuriant water-weed, wire, and other debris all pose a hazard to the underwater swimmer. The diver should be well acquainted with the area and proceed with caution if doubt exists. Avoid diving where visibility is poor.

Power craft. " 'Stop, look, and listen' before surfacing" is an excellent rule for fresh water divers. Small lakes and even rivers are used extensively by power boat enthusiasts. A boat motor can clearly be heard under water, although direction is difficult to fix. It is here that the colored float should by all means be used as a warning to boat operators that divers are in the vicinity. The "Diver's Flag" should be displayed prominently.

NOTE: If possible, avoid diving where power boats will be found.

FIG. 63. ASCEND WITH CAUTION

Moving water. Fast-moving streams are not generally considered good diving areas. Stay well away from dam spillways, floodgates, or other drain channels or pipes.

Storms. Some lakes are characterized by sudden violent storms accompanied by high winds which may raise large wind chops or waves. Residents of the area will frequently give information relative to these dangers.

Soft mud. It is possible to sink deeply into soft-mud bottoms. Here again, knowledge of the area is important.

Wandering off. If diving is a part of a camp activity, avoid wandering off on solitary exploratory trips. Stay with the group, keep track of your buddy, and return immediately upon being called.

Diving From Craft

It is always desirable if possible to have some type of craft at or near the diving spot. Paddle boards, skiffs, outboard motorboats, inboard motorboats, and even canoes are used. Your buddy may handle the boat and, in the case of smaller craft, can stay right alongside the diver as long as he stays in calm water. Game taken can be placed directly into the boat, and clothing and refreshments can be right at hand following the dive.

CHOOSING THE CRAFT

Paddle board. Most boards are satisfactory, and lines or strips of inner tube can be secured to hold tools and game sacks. Some users have cut a hole through the board so that the diver can place his face in the water and still be dry until ready to dive. Built-in glass plates are usually unsatisfactory. The board should not leak.

Using the paddle board. Although a one-man craft, a board can be used by two successfully. Most accidents to paddle-board users occur in the surf line. Experience will help to avoid this type of trouble.

The choice of other craft is governed by what is available. With powered craft, however, the operator must cut the motor and avoid moving the rudder when divers are entering or leaving the water. If moving near to a diver the operator must lie off at a safe distance. A short ladder should be provided for entering the boat.

Marine Life

The "tidal zone," although partly beyond the reach of the free diver (skin or scuba) using present-day equipment, supports the abundance of the ocean's available supply of food from the smallest to the largest form of life.

One-celled plants called "diatoms," microscopic in size, utilize the silica washed down by the rivers. Other microscopic organisms called "dinoflagellates," animal larvae, and a myriad of small floating animals which feed on the diatoms are collectively called "plankton."

Plankton is the food of larger sea life, even whales and some of the shark family.

Most of the inhabitants of the sea feed upon one another, thereby preventing overpopulation. Thus is established a balanced community under the sea. Man observes this balance and wisely (in most instances), either by law or by agreement, does not upset it. As on land, the variety and abundance of life is determined by environment, temperature, and the availability of food. Even slight temperature changes have a marked effect on sea life; therefore most forms are restricted to certain temperature areas.

There are so many varied pursuits open to newcomers to the underwater world that each is worthy of a thorough study. Geology, photography, spear fishing, zoology, marine biology, archaeology, treasure hunting, or just plain sightseeing are full-time, paying jobs for many. Whether professional or amateur, all are wise to become acquainted with certain of the creatures of the underwater world.

Sharks, barracuda, moray eels, octopus, squid—poisonous, injurious, or otherwise-menacing forms of animal and plant life are a constant source of tall tales (some not so tall), and so they rate more than a bit of investigation. The following information is based upon marine science, purposeful experimentation, and authenticated reports. The order in which they are presented must not be construed as the order of importance.

SHARKS

The much-discussed villain of many sea stories is a many-specied holdover from prehistoric life. He is the possessor of a tough hide, cartilaginous skeleton, and nearly unpredictable nature. The species runs the gamut of size from the spiny dogfish to the huge whale shark. They inhabit all the warm seas and even move into the cooler waters of the world during the summer seasons in the temperate zones. Their appetites are as varied as the species. The following brief description of commoner varieties will give an idea of their spread.

Whale shark—length 35 to 60 feet—identified by checkerboard formation of lines on its back dotted with white spots—feeds on plankton and other minute sea life—inhabits all seas. Considered harmless unless attacked.

Basking shark—length up to 45 feet—gray-brown back—usually seen floating lazily on surface—feeds on small crustaceans and copepods—found in all warm seas.

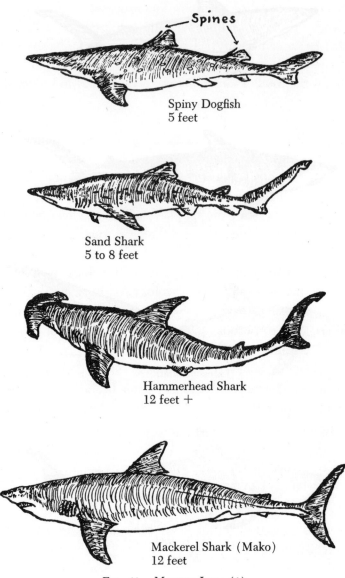

FIG. 64.   MARINE LIFE (1)

Blue shark—length 12 feet—deep blue on dorsal side—heavy shouldered and stout—feeds on fish—usually found in warm seas—considered by many to be a man-eater.

White shark—length 30 feet—black or slate gray but may occur as leaden white entirely—feeds on large fish and turtles—found in warm, temperate seas, usually in deep water but often in shallower water also (hunger or injury causes this). This species is reputed to be a man-eater, but few authentic reports exist to support the statement.

Thresher shark—length 15 feet—characterized by long scythe-shaped

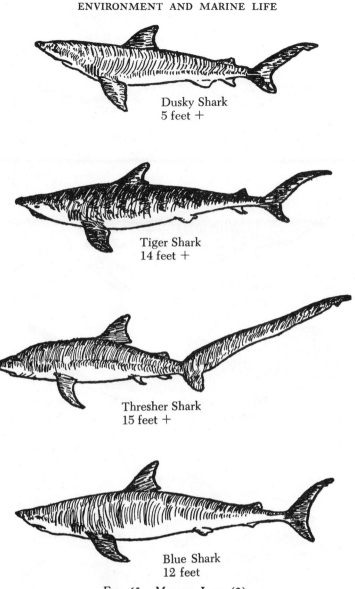

Dusky Shark
5 feet +

Tiger Shark
14 feet +

Thresher Shark
15 feet +

Blue Shark
12 feet

FIG. 65. MARINE LIFE (2)

upper half of caudal fin—usually work in pairs destroying schools of fish—found in all temperate seas.

Tiger shark—length 12 to 30 feet—distinguished by large head and convex snout overhanging wide jaws full of sickle-shaped teeth—dark tigerlike stripes visible on sides when young—feeds on large fish, turtles, carrion—found in warm temperate and tropical seas—although feared by natives in some areas, no authenticated reports exist to support man-eater theory.

Hammerhead shark—length 12 to 17 feet—easily distinguished by unusual head shaped like flattened tack hammer with eyes at outer portion—usually swims with dorsal and upper half of caudal fin visible above surface

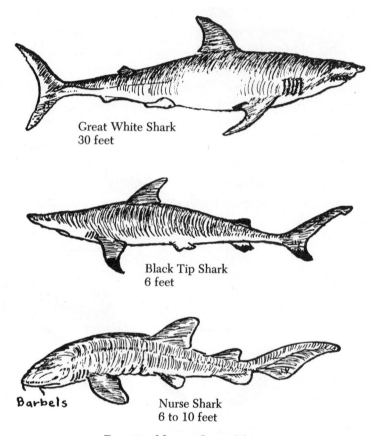

Brown Shark (rel. to Blue and Tiger Sharks)
8 feet

Great White Shark
30 feet

Black Tip Shark
6 feet

Barbels   Nurse Shark
6 to 10 feet

FIG. 66.   MARINE LIFE (3)

—feeds on fish, squid, clams, and barnacles. Perhaps because of the elongated nostrils in front of "hammer" he is, if near by, the first on the scene where blood is spilled—ill tempered but we know of no verified human attacks.

Sand shark—length 3 to 10 feet—commonest variety—gray, spotted with brown—fins may be edged with black—large dorsal fin and second, uneven dorsal toward tail—feeds on small fish—usually found close to shore and in bays and harbors—inhabits warm waters in winter and temperate zones when water warms in summer—swims slowly with dorsal and upper caudal fins showing. This species is considered harmless.

Nurse shark—length 6 to 10 feet—distinguished by large dorsal fin and small barbel on each side of the mouth—feeds on squid and shrimp—usually found on bottom in shallow water. It is nonaggressive.

Spiny dogfish—3 to 6 feet—slate colored—has sharp spike placed before each of the dorsal fins—has rounded head and flat snout—a nuisance to commercial fishermen.

Mako shark—length 12 feet—fast—streamlined—has pointed snout and long teeth—found in coastal areas and considered a good game fish because of its activity when hooked. (Also called *mackerel shark*.)

Because of the variety of species of sharks and their unpredictable behavior, no hard and fast rules for handling an encounter can be laid down to apply in every case. Sharks may display a great degree of curiosity or passive interest, or they may completely ignore a skin or scuba diver. They may be easily frightened away by yelling underwater, banging on air tanks, advancing toward them boldly, jabbing at them with spear or "shark billy" (a short, weighted club) or merely by causing a quantity of air bubbles to frighten or puzzle them. Repeated encounters with sharks of all species or hearing of these encounters may lead the uninitiated to believe the shark is an overgrown bully or coward and easily scared off, but such is not always the case.

FIG. 67. TROUBLE

Do not carry speared fish close to the body. Tow your catch on a minimum of 20 feet of line, or better yet, remove it from the water immediately. Remove yourself from the vicinity of any spilled blood. If your catch is seriously disputed, give it up if the shark doesn't seem inclined to be frightened off. If you are injured or bleeding, get out of the water as soon as possible (whether sharks are present or not). If visibility is poor, don't push your luck (several authentic reports of attack have given this as a prime cause of attack, whether through error or poor vision on the part of the shark). In conclusion, if a retreat becomes the better part of valor, swim slowly backward (facing the menace) submerged until safety is reached. Also remember that a shark doesn't have to turn over to bite.

Authenticated reports of shark attacks on man have led to the conclusion that man has not been the prime target. In nearly every case there was either blood, injured fish, or some piece of equipment or apparel which might have resembled a fish, or the water was murky.

WHALES

Whales are mammals and rarely visit shallow water. They are not a problem to the skin or scuba diver. There is one agreed exception:

Killer whale (dolphin)—length 25 feet—toothed, voracious, and a definite potential menace—identified by the oversized dorsal fin (higher than the shark's dorsal fin and horizontal caudal fins—no authentic reports of attack found *but* records of their attack on herds of seal and other large creatures should be warning enough. Leave the water if the killer whale is sighted.

FIG. 68.   KILLER WHALE (ORCA)
Dolphin Family (Grampus)

BARRACUDA

Next to shark (or ahead, depending on how you feel) these are perhaps the most feared of the undersea predators. This fear, where it exists, is not altogether unwarranted because of the potential damage which the fish can inflict. There have been many authentic reports of attack by the "cuda."

Fig. 69. Great Barracuda
10 feet

However, as is true of sharks, in almost all cases it could be assumed from evidence that the attacks were due entirely to presence of blood from an injured fish or a human being, bright or shiny lurelike equipment, mistaken identity because of poor visibility, or disturbance and bubbles caused by surface swimming. The barracuda will swim over, alongside of, or around the diver and may only be tempted to rush in when a fish is speared. Then he is not so respectful, and if the catch is disputed he may easily remove fingers or adjacent parts along with the fish.

Barracuda will usually retreat from the presence of a diver if the diver makes a bold advance. The larger the fish the less easily he scares; and sometimes a slow retreat of the diver is the better part of valor—no headlong, splashy, surface retreat but a slow deceitful back-pedaling type.

Stick to the rules concerning visibility, clothing, equipment, blood, and injured fish. If you don't panic, the barracuda will probably be just another of the inquisitive members of the underwater population.

There are twenty or more species of barracuda, but only one, the *great barracuda,* is of any concern to the skin and scuba diver. Ranging from 3 to 10 feet long, the fish is long and cylindrically built for speed. Its wedge-shaped head (about one fourth of the body length) is half occupied by the mouth with its jutting lower jaw and filled with a series of fanglike teeth, knife-edged front and rear grinders. These are displayed almost constantly since the barracuda has two mouth vents which permit him to swim with mouth open. The coloring, though changeable with environment, is usually dark green or blue on top, sides silver or yellow, and the belly white. Dark bars and blotches mark the back and sides. It may be found around wharves, buoys, coral beds, and wrecks, usually near the surface. The usual range of the great barracuda is the West Indies and the coast of Florida.

Moray Eel

Moray eel species have interjected themselves in choice bits of history dating back many years. Morays were kept in ponds or pits and fed the owner's enemies or slaves. The Romans kept them as pets, and of them Cicero was moved to write: "They deemed no moment of their lives more happy than when these creatures first came to eat out of their hands." More recently, skin divers (of the hardy type) have handled these sharp-toothed, slippery creatures without coming to grief.

Like so many creatures of the sea, the moray becomes dangerous only when his nest is invaded or when he is injured.

The six-foot *green moray* is covered with thick, leathery skin. The basic color is bluish slate but is covered with a yellow mucus thereby blending to green. Some brownish or slate-colored specimens may be observed, since there is an absence of yellow in the mucus. They are usually found in holes or crevices of the reefs of the West Indies and Florida Keys.

Three species of spotted morays, usually 2 or 3 feet long, are found as far north as Charleston, South Carolina. Still another which inhabits deep water may be found as far north as New England. The Pacific moray eel ranges off the southern coast of California.

The moray poses no problem to the skin diver unless he carelessly puts his hand into a hole or crevice without first cautiously assuring himself of its contents.

Octopus

The octopus has been the villain in many an ancient sailor's tale, its size greatly magnified and its aggressiveness related to be so great that whole ships were pulled under by its tentacles. Skin divers all over the world have found no evidence to support such tales. The octopus is nonaggressive and, except for the largest of the species which may measure 20 feet from arm tip to arm tip, usually are small, timid, and, because of nocturnal habits, seldom seen. Handling of the octopus should be done carefully so as to avoid the center-placed beak, which secretes a venom with which it paralyzes its prey.

Squid

The squid has ten arms, two longer than the others, and, unlike the octopus, swims about. It is capable of inflicting severe bites with its beak when annoyed or caught. Because of its size, the giant squid, which grows in excess of 50 feet, may well be responsible for the atrocities placed at the door of the peaceful octopus.

Rays

The ray family gives little trouble to the skin diver. The *sting ray* because of the barbed spines at the base of the tail can inflict a painful wound if stepped on or if lashing about when speared. These stab wounds are prone to become infected and should receive medical attention immediately. When entering the water or moving about in shallow areas, shuffling the swim fins on the bottom will usually scare away the rays in the vicinity. Another

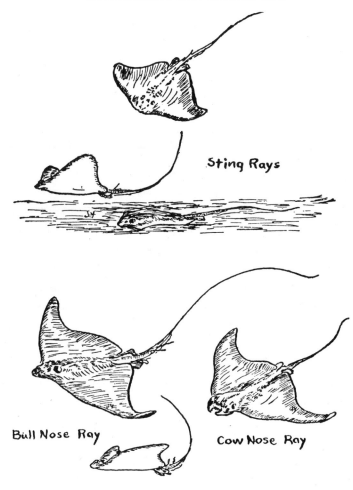

FIG. 70. TYPES OF RAYS

species, *torpedo ray*, often found on sandy bottoms off northern California, is equipped with an organ capable of giving an electric shock severe enough to stun large fish. Despite these defenses the entire ray family is nonaggressive and will avoid contact with the skin diver.

COELENTERATES

Less mobile but equally dangerous and annoying are the coelenterates which include jellyfish, sea anemones, most coral polyps, and the *Portuguese man-of-war*. The latter is a colony of specialized organisms making up what appears to be a single individual. These sea creatures are capable of stinging, with varying intensity, the unwary diver coming in contact with the tentacles. The sting of the Portuguese man-of-war is often severe enough to make hospitalization necessary. Having been once stung, the diver may be more seriously affected if stung again.

The Portuguese man-of-war is easily identified by the brilliant iridescent float which may attain a length of 12 inches and may have attached tentacles of 40 feet in length.

Jellyfish vary in size from 1 inch to 12 feet in diameter with tentacles streaming down several inches or many feet below the umbrella-shaped body. During late spring and summer, when the waters are warm, these free-swimming coelenterates are quite numerous in rivers, bays, and, to a lesser extent, open water.

Contacting the tentacles of the jellyfish will cause a wide variety of discomforts to the diver, from mild local stings to violent systemic disturbances (the latter is rare). Since they are difficult to avoid, especially in limited visibility areas, protective clothing in the form of wet or dry suits or just plain long johns should be worn if their presence is detected.

Coral, with its brilliant hues and beautiful formations, is made up of many millions of living and dead polyps of the coelenterate family. Utilizing the calcium deposits in the water, a small shell-like cup is built at the base. As the polyps reproduce and die, successive layers of these shells are developed in varying forms, from tree or plantlike structures to the great coral reefs. Beautiful as coral may be, it can be a menace to the diver because of the fine razorlike edges it presents. Scratches or cuts received should be cared for immediately to prevent infection. Coral stings, particularly from "fire coral," are annoying if not dangerous and should be cared for.

OTHERS

Sea urchins belong to the family of starfish and sea cucumber but are considerably more annoying. They are equipped with needlelike spines, and may be found as large as 7 inches in diameter. This spiny, animated burr may be found on the bottom in all warm waters.

Because of their sharpness the spines of the sea urchin will penetrate skin and often break off. Every effort should be made to extract the spines as soon as possible and the puncture wound should be immediately cared for to prevent infection.

Scorpion fish of the Pacific Ocean and Red Sea are spiny-finned, and they secrete a poison which can be painful or fatal to man. They are usually found on bottom among stones and vegetation.

Sea snakes—usually brilliantly colored with flattened tails—may be seen in tropical waters. They secrete a nerve poison similar to the cobra and coral snakes, but they are timid and will bite only when attacked.

Mollusks (clams, mussels, oysters, snails, abalones)—particularly those in quiet waters—have sharp or serrated edges which are capable of inflicting painful and easily infected wounds. Gloves should be worn when collecting any of these.

Barnacles and *tube worms* have sharp, hard shells and can also inflict easily infected wounds if contacted.

Crabs and *lobsters* have specialized equipment for capturing their food. The unwary diver may find himself painfully attached to even one of the smaller species. The larger species are capable of breaking or even severing a finger with their large claws.

Wear gloves and arm yourself with knowledge of how to capture your prey lest *you* be caught. Local divers usually develop nearly safe procedures and will share their knowledge.

Seal, sea lion, manatee—although normally not a menace to the diver— may be aggressive to the danger point if they are guarding the harem, or if a herd is nearby. Avoid areas of large groups and stay out of trouble.

PLANT GROWTH

In the form of *seaweed* or *kelp* it can be annoying or even dangerous if encountered in concentration. Rising from the bottom, kelp may spread out and cover large areas of the surface. *Eel grass* may be long enough to entangle equipment because of surge, since it is found at the surf line.

A diver coming up in kelp should keep the hands overhead, part the kelp, and look for a clear area, then drop feet first and swim to the clear area underwater. Attempting to swim on top of kelp or grass will only result in serious entanglement.

If entangled, remain calm and methodically disentangle yourself and equipment, drop below, and swim to a clear area. Using force will get the same results as pulling hard on the end of a backlashed line.

FOOD FISH

Food fish of particular interest to the spearfishing, skin, or scuba diver are so numerous in species and habitat that local divers should be consulted or Fish and Wildlife booklets obtained and read before diving so as to comply with custom and law. Also, fish that is good to eat in one area may not be edible in another. A planned activity usually gives best results.

Since skin and scuba divers are becoming more numerous, and many will, because of lack of knowledge, take any fish which becomes a target for the spear, there will be an increased number of sick feasters.

Ichthyotoxism (internal poisoning due to consumption of fish) resembles food poisoning. The symptoms occur from a short time after the meal to ten hours later and may vary in intensity, depending on how poisonous was the fish and how big the meal. Nausea, vomiting, abdominal cramps, and diarrhea, even numbness, paralysis, or impairment of the senses may be present in part or entirely.

Since little is known of this particular poisoning effect, the best treatment is prevention. Consult local information sources to ascertain the presence of poisonous species. If symptoms appear, large quantities of water by mouth will help to flush the alimentary tract and speed recovery.

All cases should be brought to the attention of a physician as soon as possible.

A *parasite* known as the flat fish tapeworm has one of its intermediate life cycles in the muscle of the fresh water fish. It can be dangerous to human beings only if the fish is eaten raw. Cooking destroys this parasite.

9

PLANNING A SCUBA DIVE

The simplicity with which scuba can be utilized by individuals with only minimum essential training by no means reduces the hazards intrinsic in diving. Simplicity of operation is no measure of safety. On the contrary, it tends to develop within the individual a false sense of proficiency which can lead to disaster. The early development of safe scuba diving habits predicated upon sound knowledge of the basic laws pertaining to the physics and physiology of diving is essential to counteract this incipient danger.

Safe scuba diving habits are assured when sound knowledge and good judgment are exercised in planning a scuba dive. Plans need not be elaborate or restrictive but should provide for a systematic means to consider essential elements of diving safety. The essential elements are those which determine whether or not a scuba dive can be conducted without endangering human life. The purpose of this chapter is to present and discuss these essential elements as they affect the individual, the environment, and the scuba. Planning a scuba dive ensures maximum safety within the means available.

The Individual

The individual is the foundation upon which safe scuba diving procedures have been formulated, but they are of value only insofar as the individual demonstrates a willingness to implement them. Safe diving procedures are not new; they are established techniques based upon long experience and scientific study by scientists, doctors, professional divers, and in particular the United States Navy. The safety record established and maintained by our Navy in deep- and shallow-water diving is above reproach and one every scuba diver should endeavor to match.

In planning a scuba dive, consideration should be given to the individual's physical capacity or fitness to perform the dive. Physical fitness should include periodic physical examinations to ascertain the individual's state of health and assurance by a qualified medical doctor that scuba diving will not be harmful or injurious. Prior to the actual performance of a dive, the scuba diver should have obtained adequate sleep and abstained from alcoholic beverages; and under no circumstances should he dive while under the influence of alcohol, sedatives, or any drug which impairs alertness. Diving with a common cold, ear fungi or infection, external skin abrasions, or similar indisposition should be avoided. The damage which may result to the upper respiratory system, the middle ear, or other portions of the anatomy could cause permanent disability. Scuba divers should exercise regularly, utilizing exercises which demand physical exertion and endurance, and which may provide an opportunity to increase their proficiency in the water. A partial list of recommended exercises might include distance swims with fins and face masks, skin diving, water polo, cross-country running, and other active athletic endeavors. Good health habits and exercises plus periodic physical examinations will ensure the individual's physical fitness for scuba diving.

No less important than physical fitness is mental fitness. The individual should have a sincere desire to perform a scuba dive and should have demonstrated the quality of emotional stability. The unfamiliar natural phenomena to be encountered in the fluid, comparatively silent world underwater coupled with the scuba diver's own awareness of his solitude may create panic reactions even in voluntary divers. Individuals who coerce, shame, or ridicule another into involuntarily performing a scuba dive are inducing others to risk self-destruction needlessly. Unfortunately, specific rules cannot be applied which will positively determine an individual's mental fitness or emotional stability in reference to scuba diving. Certain factors can give an indication as to mental fitness for diving and should be subjected to a critical evaluation by the individual concerned. These factors include a sincere desire to dive, no personal history of or tendency toward claustrophobia, no fear of darkness or isolation, an alert mind capable of formulating and implementing decisions, respect for danger, and a capability for normal fear reactions without a tendency to panic. Very few emergencies arise in scuba diving that cannot be successfully concluded with the proper timely application of corrective actions. Physical and mental fitness offer the best assurance that an individual can competently and expeditiously extricate himself from a hazardous or untenable circumstance.

The next essential element to be considered and evaluated in planning a scuba dive consists of the individual's academic knowledge of the theory of diving, aquatic proficiency, and experience in scuba diving. These factors, aside from the physical and physiological limitations, necessitate the establishment of safe boundaries commensurate with the degree of knowledge, training, and skill possessed by the individual. When planning a scuba dive, the individual must carefully evaluate these factors and establish safe boundaries. Clubs and other organizations will find it useful to establish a classification of divers on the basis of their knowledge, aquatic proficiency, and experience. The following is offered as a suggested rating scale:

A. The NOVICE is an individual who is attempting this endeavor for the first time or who has limited knowledge of the physics and physiology of diving, possesses only meager aquatic proficiency, or is unfamiliar with scuba equipment. Novice scuba divers should confine their activity to indoor swimming pools under the supervision of a competent scuba diving instructor.

B. The second degree, or classification of skills, which may be applied to scuba divers in general is that of INTERMEDIATE diver. This individual has achieved adequate knowledge of the theory of diving, demonstrated sufficient aquatic proficiency, and become familiar with the operation of scuba equipment. Experience in scuba diving is inadequate. Intermediate scuba divers should restrict their diving to optimum environmental conditions and to accomplish open water training under the supervision of a capable, experienced scuba diver.

C. Continuing the classification of skills essential to the scuba diver necessitates the listing of criteria for qualification as a SENIOR scuba diver. This designation represents the accomplishment of outstanding proficiency with reference to knowledge of the theory of diving, aquatic ability, and acquisition of actual open-water scuba diving experience. In addition, the Senior diver must exercise the fundamentals of good leadership, and must accept personal responsibility for the safety of individuals with inferior knowledge, ability, or experience. The Senior scuba diver sets the example and insists on the establishment of safe scuba diving procedures based on sound knowledge of the essential elements and the application of good judgment predicated upon a continuous systematic evaluation of the diving conditions as they exist. When a Senior scuba diver is accompanied on a scuba dive by a Novice or Intermediate scuba diver, the restrictions applicable to the lesser qualifications must apply to ensure maximum safety to all concerned.

The next consideration in planning a scuba dive after determining that the individual scuba diver is physically, mentally, and technically qualified to dive within prescribed boundaries is to evaluate those essential elements of diving safety which must be accomplished in conjunction with another scuba diver. No live scuba diver has ever been or should ever consider himself to be a completely self-sufficient, self-sustaining individual. Those essential elements of diving safety which must be considered, evaluated, and established with another individual in planning a scuba dive are: the "Buddy" System, the Underwater Communications System, and the Emergency Assistance Plan.

The Buddy System

The buddy system is a mandatory safety diving procedure which must be recognized, understood, and established prior to each and every scuba dive. Quite simply defined, it means that no individual scuba diver, regardless of proficiency or experience, should ever undertake a scuba dive alone but must in the interest of self-preservation be accompanied by at least one other similarly qualified scuba diver who has acknowledged and accepted the responsibility for the safety of his partner under any circumstances requiring mutual assistance.

FIG. 71.   NEVER DIVE ALONE

1. To facilitate the most effective safety measures when utilizing the buddy system demands the utmost confidence in each other's knowledge, ability, and judgment, and the strict observance of a well-defined swimmer-distance range. Swimmer-distance range is that distance which separates one buddy from another during performance of a scuba dive. This range may vary dependent upon the time, depth, and circumstance, but should never exceed the limits of actual visual contact. During daylight hours in shallow, clear water it is permissible for the swim buddy to be a properly equipped,

proficient surface swimmer. Scuba dives at night or in conditions of limited visibility should be avoided. If the circumstances warrant a night scuba dive, swim buddies should maintain contact one with the other by utilizing a "buddy line." This technique requires two swimmers to be tied together by a line 6 to 10 feet long over which they can transmit simple signals relative to their circumstance and the objective of the dive.

FIG. 72. DIVING AT NIGHT OR IN MURKY WATER

2. The mutual protection and responsibility accepted by swim buddies also requires the observance of rules of underwater conduct. These rules should include:

(a) Signaling intended actions, such as ascent, descent, and change of direction. Such signals must be mutually understood so that the intended actions may be executed simultaneously.

(b) Signaling when visual contact is lost by banging on scuba cylinders with metal or rock, listening for a reply in similar fashion, or for the breathing noise of the other's scuba unit. Surfacing if rapid reestablishment of visual contact is not made.

(c) Signaling at the earliest possible moment any circumstance or situation which might create a hazardous or untenable condition.

(d) Providing confidence and reassurance of a buddy in a hazardous or undesirable situation while maintaining calm self-control and implementing proper corrective action.

(e) Coordinating and achieving mutual agreement and understanding of the communications signals to be employed, the depth-time limitation to be observed, and the underwater activities contemplated.

The Underwater Communications System

The communications system to be employed by scuba divers should offer a simple means to convey ideas and direct actions between individuals underwater or with a surface tender. Signals must not be complicated or easily misunderstood, but may vary to meet specific objectives. The significant factor regardless of the communications system employed is that complete understanding can be maintained by swim buddies surfaced or submerged during all scuba diving operations. The most readily available method of underwater communications for scuba divers is a system composed of hand or line signals. Hand and line signals have been employed by military and commercial organizations in diving operations with considerable success for decades, and may still be considered the scuba diver's most effective means of communications. The following signals are adopted in part, for scuba divers, from the United States Navy standard system of naval signals, as published in the *Bureau of Ships Diving Manual*. Their effectiveness in controlling underwater activities has been positively established by their contribution to thousands of hours of accident-free naval diving operations. They serve as a guide which the intelligent scuba diver will follow.

LINE SIGNALS

From scuba diver A to scuba diver B or from surface tender to scuba diver

1 pull	"Are you all right?" or, when going down, "Stop."
2 pulls	"Going down."
3 pulls	"Stand by to come up."
4 pulls	"Come up."
2 pulls, pause, 1 pull	"I understand you."

From scuba diver B to scuba diver A in reply or scuba diver to surface tender

1 pull	"I am all right."
2 pulls	"Going down." or "Lower me."
3 pulls	"Stand by to come up." or "Take up my slack line."
4 pulls	"Coming up." or "Haul me up."
2 pulls, pause, 1 pull	"I understand you."

LINE EMERGENCY SIGNALS

2–2–2 pulls	"I am fouled and need your assistance."
3–3–3 pulls	"I am fouled but do not need your assistance."
4–4–4 pulls	"Take me up."

HAND SIGNALS

1. Thumbs up — "I intend to go up."
2. Thumbs down — "I intend to go down."
3. Hand points horizontal direction — "I intend to go that way."
4. Point to mouthpiece and then remove — "I need air."
5. Point to compass — "Which way from here?"
6. Point to watch — "Time to ascend."
7. One or both hands palm up — "What's next?" or "Question."

HAND EMERGENCY SIGNALS

1. Banging on cylinder with metal or rock — "Attention!" or "Join me."
2. Hand drawn knifelike across the throat — "I am fouled; need your assistance."
3. One or both hands clutch throat — "I'm hurt; take me up."

The use of hand or line signals does not allow the transmission of complicated messages or instructions. It does provide a simple system which can be codified and memorized by the individuals for use in a variety of circumstances. It must be absolutely understood and diligently practiced by swim buddies and/or surface tenders before commencing a dive. All signals must be promptly answered or returned exactly as given. Thus, a positive means of determining that the signal has been received and correctly understood is gained. A communications system properly utilized does much to reduce the hazards of scuba diving and is of great comfort to the wary scuba diver apprehensive of isolation or solitude.

The Emergency Assistance Plan

The emergency assistance plan should be formulated simultaneously with the selection of swim buddies and/or tenders and the adoption of a communications system. The selection of swim buddies and the establishment of communications are in fact two basics essential to rendering effective emergency assistance. It is not feasible to define each specific emergency which may be encountered in scuba diving and recommend positive corrective measures to be applied in each circumstance. Rather, it is better to depend on the intelligence of the individuals and offer guidelines which have application to many emergencies.

Effective emergency assistance plans will make provision for one man, ideally the most proficient scuba diver accompanying the diving party, to exercise complete supervision over the dive and the divers. This individual should maintain supervision from a surface craft or position, and be completely equipped to render emergency assistance at a moment's notice. The instructions of the dive supervisor must be clear, concise, and instantaneously obeyed before, during, and after a scuba dive, but emphatically so during actual emergencies. It must be clearly understood that the dive supervisor occupies the position of authority. In addition to his other responsibilities the supervisor should know the location and nature of all natural and manmade hazards in the vicinity of the diving site and caution all divers accordingly. He should also know the name, location, and telephone number of those organizations which can render emergency assistance, such as police departments, fire departments, lifesaving stations, first aid stations, hospitals, and the nearest recompression chamber.

Personnel within the scuba diving group must be accomplished in the techniques of artificial respiration and first aid. Equipment essential to lifesaving must be at hand. Scuba diving accidents seldom just happen; they are caused by inadequate knowledge, ability, experience, planning, or preparation. Most underwater situations which are likely to cause accidents can be anticipated. Planning can prevent an unfavorable circumstance from developing into an accident or fatality. The greatest danger of all is to be emotionally, physically, or materially unprepared to render emergency assistance when a life may be in the balance.

The Scuba Dive

In planning a scuba dive, the essential elements of diving safety applicable to scuba units must be systematically considered and evaluated to ensure the safety of the individual. These essential elements include the reliability of the scuba, calculation of the air supply, its certified purity, determination of the unit's proper functioning, operation of the mechanical safety features, and care and storage of equipment.

One of the essential elements with respect to the scuba itself is its inherent reliability. Reliability means that it will function as intended with only a minute possibility of mechanical failure. Adequate standards of reliability seldom, if ever, can be obtained in any homemade rig or with components designed for other purposes. One safe standard that can be applied in determining the reliability of scuba units is to accept for diving only those commercial types which have actually been accepted for use by the United States Navy. Unfortunately, however, advertising statements implying that such approval has been given or that Navy standards have been met cannot always be taken at face value. The Navy evaluates apparatus only for its own purposes and in no case publicly approves or disapproves commercial items. No manufacturer is authorized to use "Navy Approval" as an advertising claim. There is a real need for an impartial civilian-testing and standard-setting organization to guide buyers and to help keep unsatisfactory apparatus off the market.

Plans for scuba diving should provide for adequate time and consideration of the requirements for a predive test of the scuba to determine its ability

FIG. 73. INSPECT BEFORE YOU DIVE

to function properly. During this predive test, the manufacturer's instruction book on proper care, maintenance, and function should be consulted to ensure that proper attention is given to any peculiarities of a specific unit. The following predive test items are applicable to any of the current-type open-circuit air breathing apparatuses.

A. Ascertain that the cylinders contain only certified pure breathing air. Air which contains contaminants such as carbon monoxide can cause serious trouble, even death.

B. Know the pressure in the cylinders before each dive. Calculate the depth-time limitation for the deepest depth contemplated. Include the decompression time, if any, and a positive margin of safety. Whenever possible, plan each dive to avoid the necessity of decompression. Exceeding the depth-time limitations without adequate provision for decompression is especially foolhardy when adequate facilities for recompression treatment of bends are not immediately available.

C. Immediately preceding the dive, while still on the surface, the individual using the particular scuba should ascertain by personal inspection that the main high-pressure valve is open and that the demand valve regulator is functioning properly. This simple test can be accomplished by breathing several times with all diving controls positioned for submerged operations. Any malfunctions or imperfections in operations, such as hard breathing, erratic valve fluctuations, or loose fittings, justify suspending the diving plans until proper corrective measures have been applied.

D. Mechanical safety features on most contemporary-type scuba units include a reserve air feature and a quick-release harness assembly. The individual utilizing the scuba should be double-checked by his swim buddy on the operation of the reserve air feature and the proper assembly of the harness quick-release feature. The actual operation of both these safety features should then be demonstrated to the dive supervisor who should personally check that the reserve air supply control valve is in the off position. The pre-dive test can then be concluded by a shallow dive in the immediate vicinity of the diving site to ascertain that the units are properly functioning before descending to the desired depth and task.

E. Planning a scuba dive does not end with the descent of the diver into the depths. The plan must also include provision for the proper care and storage of the equipment upon completion of the dive. Generally, the accomplishment of a few simple tasks will ensure the readiness of equipment for the next day of diving. Upon surfacing, the individual should first close all high-pressure valves. If this is the concluding dive of the operation, then in sequence the following steps should be accomplished:

1. Wash the scuba in fresh water, being careful to stop the high-pressure inlet on the demand valve regulator.
2. Clean all rubber components of grease, oil, or other organic solvents.
3. Drain and dry the apparatus.
4. Store the equipment in a clean, safe place where the cylinders can be protected from dropping, sharp blows, and excessive heat.

DIVE SAFELY, THE LIFE YOU SAVE *WILL* BE YOUR OWN!

Safety and survival underwater are achieved by careful planning. This must be based on a good understanding of the environment, the equipment, and the limitations of the individual.

APPENDIX

United States Navy Air Decompression Tables

TABLE 1–4. DECOMPRESSION PROCEDURES

GENERAL INSTRUCTIONS FOR AIR DIVING

Need for Decompression

A quantity of nitrogen is taken up by the body during every dive. The amount absorbed depends upon the depth of the dive and the exposure (bottom) time. If the quantity of nitrogen dissolved in the body tissues exceeds a certain critical amount, the ascent must be delayed to allow the body tissue to remove the excess nitrogen. Decompression sickness results from failure to delay the ascent and to allow this process of gradual desaturation. A specified time at a specific depth for purposes of desaturation is called a decompression stop.

"No Decompression" Schedules

Dives that are not long or deep enough to require decompression stops are "no decompression" dives. Dives to 33 feet or less do not require decompression stops. As the depth increases, the allowable bottom time for "no decompression" dives decreases. Five minutes at 190 feet is the shortest and deepest "no decompression" schedule. These dives are all listed in the No Decompression Limits and Repetitive Group Designation Table for "No Decompression" Dives, ("No Decompression Table" (table 1-6)) and only require compliance with the 60 feet per minute rate of ascent.

Schedules That Require Decompression Stops

All dives beyond the limits of the "No Decompression Table" require decompression stops. These dives are listed in the Navy Standard Air Decompression Table (table 1-5). Comply exactly with instructions except as modified by surface decompression procedures.

Variations in Rate of Ascent

Ascend from all dives at the rate of 60 feet per minute.
In the event you exceed the 60 feet per minute rate:
(1) If no decompression stops are required, but the bottom time places you within 10 minutes of a schedule that does require decompression; stop at 10 feet for the time that you should have taken in ascent at 60 feet per minute.
(2) If decompression is required; stop 10 feet below the first listed decompression depth for the time that you should have taken in ascent at 60 feet per minute.
In the event you are unable to maintain the 60 feet per minute rate of ascent:
(1) If the delay was at or near the bottom; add to the bottom time, the additional time used in ascent. Decompress according to the requirements of the total bottom time. This is the safer procedure.
(2) If the delay was near the surface; increase the first stop by the difference between the time consumed in ascent and the time that should have been consumed at 60 feet per minute.

Repetitive Dive Procedure

A dive performed within 12 hours of surfacing from a previous dive is a repetitive dive. The period between dives is the surface interval. Excess nitrogen requires 12 hours to effectively be lost from the body. These tables are designed to protect the diver from the effects of this residual nitrogen. Allow a minimum surface interval of 10 minutes between all dives. Specific instructions are given for the use of each table in the following order:
(1) The "No Decompression Table" or the Navy Standard Air Decompression Table gives the repetitive group designation for all schedules which may preceed a repetitive dive.
(2) The Surface Interval Credit Table gives credit for the desaturation occurring during the surface interval.
(3) The Repetitive Dive Timetable gives the number of minutes or residual nitrogen time to add to the actual bottom time of the repetitive dive in order to obtain decompression for the residual nitrogen.
(4) The "No Decompression Table" or the Navy Standard Air Decompression Table gives the decompression required for the repetitive dive.

U.S. NAVY STANDARD AIR DECOMPRESSION TABLE

INSTRUCTIONS FOR USE

Time of decompression stops in the table is in minutes.
Enter the table at the exact or the next greater depth than the maximum depth attained during the dive. Select the listed bottom time that is exactly equal to or is next greater than the bottom time of the dive. Maintain the diver's chest as close as possible to each decompression depth for the number of minutes listed. The rate of ascent between stops is not critical. Commence timing each stop on arrival at the decompression depth and resume ascent when the specified time has lapsed.
For example – a dive to 82 feet for 36 minutes. To determine the proper decompression procedure: The next greater depth listed in this table is 90 feet. The next greater bottom time listed opposite 90 feet is 40. Stop 7 minutes at 10 feet in accordance with the 90/40 schedule.
For example – a dive to 110 feet for 30 minutes. It is known that the depth did not exceed 110 feet. To determine the proper decompression schedule: The exact depth of 110 feet is listed. The exact bottom time of 30 minutes is listed opposite 110 feet. Decompress according to the 110/30 schedule unless the dive was particularly cold or arduous. In that case, go to the 110/40, the 120/30, or the 120/40 at your own discretion. (Rev. 1958)

TABLE 1–5. U.S. NAVY STANDARD AIR DECOMPRESSION TABLE

DEPTH (ft)	BOTTOM TIME (mins)	TIME TO FIRST STOP	50	40	30	20	10	TOTAL ASCENT TIME	REPET. GROUP
40	200						0	0.7	*
	210	0.5					2	2.5	N
	230	0.5					7	7.5	N
	250	0.5					11	11.5	O
	270	0.5					15	15.5	O
	300	0.5					19	19.5	Z
50	100						0	0.8	*
	110	0.7					3	3.7	L
	120	0.7					5	5.7	M
	140	0.7					10	10.7	M
	160	0.7					21	21.7	N
	180	0.7					29	29.7	O
	200	0.7					35	35.7	O
	220	0.7					40	40.7	Z
	240	0.7					47	47.7	Z
60	60						0	1.0	*
	70	0.8					2	2.8	K
	80	0.8					7	7.8	L
	100	0.8					14	14.8	M
	120	0.8					26	26.8	N
	140	0.8					39	39.8	O
	160	0.8					48	48.8	Z
	180	0.8					56	56.8	Z
	200	0.6				1	69	70.6	Z
70	50						0	1.2	*
	60	1.0					8	9.0	K
	70	1.0					14	15.0	L
	80	1.0					18	19.0	M
	90	1.0					23	24.0	N
	100	1.0					33	34.0	N
	110	0.8				2	41	43.8	O
	120	0.8				4	47	51.8	O
	130	0.8				6	52	58.8	O
	140	0.8				8	56	64.8	Z
	150	0.8				9	61	70.8	Z
	160	0.8				13	72	85.8	Z
	170	0.8				19	79	98.8	Z
80	40						0	1.3	*
	50	1.2					10	11.2	K
	60	1.2					17	18.2	L
	70	1.2					23	24.2	M
	80	1.0				2	31	34.0	N
	90	1.0				7	39	47.0	N
	100	1.0				11	46	58.0	N
	110	1.0				13	53	67.0	O
	120	1.0				17	56	74.0	Z
	130	1.0				19	63	83.0	Z
	140	1.0				26	69	96.0	Z
	150	1.0				32	77	110.0	Z
90	30						0	1.5	*
	40	1.3					7	8.3	J
	50	1.3					18	19.3	L
	60	1.3					25	26.3	M
	70	1.2				7	30	38.2	N
	80	1.2				13	40	54.2	N
	90	1.2				18	48	67.2	O
	100	1.2				21	54	76.2	Z
	110	1.2				24	61	86.2	Z
	120	1.2				32	68	101.2	Z
	130	1.0			5	36	74	116.0	Z
100	25						0	1.7	*
	30	1.5					3	4.5	I
	40	1.5					15	16.5	K
	50	1.3				2	24	27.3	L
	60	1.3				9	28	38.3	N
	70	1.3				17	39	57.3	O
	80	1.3				23	48	72.3	O
	90	1.2			3	23	57	84.2	Z
	100	1.2			7	23	66	97.2	Z
	110	1.2			10	34	72	117.2	Z
	120	1.2			12	41	78	132.2	Z
110	20						0	1.8	*
	25	1.7					3	4.7	H
	30	1.7					7	8.7	J
	40	1.5				2	21	24.5	L
	50	1.5				8	26	35.5	M
	60	1.5				18	36	55.5	N
	70	1.3			1	23	48	73.3	O
	80	1.3			7	23	57	88.3	Z
	90	1.3			12	30	64	107.3	Z
	100	1.3			15	37	72	125.3	Z

DEPTH (ft)	BOTTOM TIME (mins)	TIME TO FIRST STOP	50	40	30	20	10	TOTAL ASCENT TIME	REPET. GROUP
120	15						0	2.0	*
	20	1.8					2	3.8	H
	25	1.8					6	7.8	I
	30	1.8					14	15.8	J
	40	1.7				5	25	31.7	L
	50	1.7				15	31	47.7	N
	60	1.5			2	22	45	70.5	O
	70	1.5			9	23	55	88.5	O
	80	1.5			15	27	63	106.5	Z
	90	1.5			19	37	74	131.5	Z
	100	1.5			23	45	80	149.5	Z
130	10						0	2.2	*
	15	2.0					1	3.0	F
	20	2.0					4	6.0	H
	25	2.0					10	12.0	J
	30	1.8				3	18	22.8	M
	40	1.8				10	25	36.8	N
	50	1.7			3	21	37	62.7	O
	60	1.7			9	23	52	85.7	Z
	70	1.7			16	24	61	102.7	Z
	80	1.5		3	19	35	72	130.5	Z
	90	1.5		8	19	45	80	153.5	Z
140	10						0	2.3	*
	15	2.2					2	4.2	G
	20	2.2					6	8.2	I
	25	2.0				2	14	18.0	J
	30	2.0				5	21	28.0	K
	40	1.8			2	16	26	45.8	N
	50	1.8			6	24	44	75.8	O
	60	1.8			16	23	56	96.8	Z
	70	1.7		4	19	32	68	124.7	Z
	80	1.7		10	23	41	79	154.7	Z
150	5						0	2.5	C
	10	2.3					1	3.3	E
	15	2.3					3	5.3	G
	20	2.2				2	7	11.2	H
	25	2.2				4	17	23.2	K
	30	2.2				8	24	34.2	L
	40	2.0			5	19	33	59.0	N
	50	2.0			12	23	51	88.0	O
	60	1.8		3	19	26	62	111.8	Z
	70	1.8		11	19	39	75	145.8	Z
	80	1.7	1	17	19	50	84	172.7	Z
160	5						0	2.7	D
	10	2.5					1	3.5	F
	15	2.3				1	4	7.3	H
	20	2.3				3	11	16.3	J
	25	2.3				7	20	29.3	K
	30	2.2			2	11	25	40.2	M
	40	2.2			7	23	39	71.2	N
	50	2.0		2	16	23	55	98.0	Z
	60	2.0		9	19	33	69	132.0	Z
	70	1.8	1	17	22	44	80	165.8	Z
170	5						0	2.8	D
	10	2.7					2	4.7	F
	15	2.5				2	5	9.5	H
	20	2.5				4	15	21.5	J
	25	2.3			2	7	23	34.3	L
	30	2.3			4	13	26	45.3	M
	40	2.2		1	10	23	45	81.2	O
	50	2.2		5	18	23	61	109.2	Z
	60	2.0	2	15	22	37	74	152.0	Z
	70	2.0	8	17	19	51	86	183.0	Z
180	5						0	3.0	D
	10	2.8					3	5.8	F
	15	2.7				3	6	11.7	I
	20	2.5			1	5	17	25.5	K
	25	2.5			3	10	24	39.5	L
	30	2.5			6	17	27	52.5	N
	40	2.3		3	14	23	50	92.3	O
	50	2.2	2	9	19	30	65	127.2	Z
	60	2.2	5	16	19	44	81	167.2	Z
190	5						0	3.2	D
	10	2.8				1	3	6.8	G
	15	2.8				4	7	13.8	I
	20	2.7			2	6	20	30.7	K
	25	2.7			5	11	25	43.7	M
	30	2.5		1	8	19	32	62.5	N
	40	2.5		8	14	23	55	102.5	O
	50	2.3	4	13	22	33	72	146.3	Z
	60	2.3	10	17	19	50	84	182.3	Z

*See table 1-6 for repetitive groups in "no decompression" dives.

Table 1–6. "No Decompression" Limits and Repetitive Group Designation Table for "No Decompression" Dives

DEPTH (ft.)	NO DECOMPRESSION LIMITS (Min.)	A	B	C	D	E	F	G	H	I	J	K	L	M	N	O
10	–	60	120	210	300											
15	–	35	70	110	160	225	350									
20	–	25	50	75	100	135	180	240	325							
25	–	20	35	55	75	100	125	160	195	245	315					
30	–	15	30	45	60	75	95	120	145	170	205	250	310			
35	310	5	15	25	40	50	60	80	100	120	140	160	190	220	270	310
40	200	5	15	25	30	40	50	70	80	100	110	130	150	170	200	
50	100	–	10	15	25	30	40	50	60	70	80	90	100			
60	60	–	10	15	20	25	30	40	50	55	60					
70	50	–	5	10	15	20	30	35	40	45	50					
80	40	–	5	10	15	20	25	30	35	40						
90	30	–	5	10	12	15	20	25	30							
100	25	–	5	7	10	15	20	22	25							
110	20	–	–	5	10	13	15	20								
120	15	–	–	5	10	12	15									
130	10	–	–	5	8	10										
140	10	–	–	5	7	10										
150	5	–	–	5												
160	5	–	–	–	5											
170	5	–	–	–	5											
180	5	–	–	–	5											
190	5	–	–	–	5											

(Rev. 1958)

INSTRUCTIONS FOR USE

I. "No decompression" limits

This column shows at various depths greater than 30 feet the allowable diving times (in minutes) which permit surfacing directly at 60 ft. a minute with no decompression stops. Longer exposure times require the use of the Standard Air Decompression Table (Table 1-5).

II. Repetitive group designation table

The tabulated exposure times (or bottom times) are in minutes. The times at the various depths in each vertical column are the maximum exposures during which a diver will remain within the group listed at the head of the column.

To find the repetitive group designation at surfacing for dives involving exposures up to and including the "no decompression limits": Enter the table on the exact or next greater depth than that to which exposed and select the listed exposure time exact or next greater than the actual exposure time. The repetitive group designation is indicated by the letter at the head of the vertical column where the selected exposure time is listed.

For example: A dive was to 32 feet for 45 minutes. Enter the table along the 35 ft. depth line since it is next greater than 32 ft. The table shows that since group "D" is left after 40 minutes exposure and group "E" after 50 minutes, group "E" (at the head of the column where the 50 min. exposure is listed) is the proper selection.

Exposure times for depths less than 40 ft. are listed only up to approximately five hours since this is considered to be beyond field requirements for this table.

TABLE 1–7. SURFACE INTERVAL CREDIT TABLE

REPETITIVE GROUP AT THE END OF THE SURFACE INTERVAL

REPETITIVE GROUP AT THE BEGINNING OF SURFACE INTERVAL (FROM PREVIOUS DIVE)

	Z	O	N	M	L	K	J	I	H	G	F	E	D	C	B	A
Z	0:10-0:22	0:34	0:48	1:02	1:18	1:36	1:55	2:17	2:42	3:10	3:45	4:29	5:27	6:56	10:05	12:00*
O		0:10-0:23	0:36	0:51	1:07	1:24	1:43	2:04	2:29	2:59	3:33	4:17	5:16	6:44	9:54	12:00*
N			0:10-0:24	0:39	0:54	1:11	1:30	1:53	2:18	2:47	3:22	4:04	5:03	6:32	9:43	12:00*
M				0:10-0:25	0:42	0:59	1:18	1:39	2:05	2:34	3:08	3:52	4:49	6:18	9:28	12:00*
L					0:10-0:26	0:45	1:04	1:25	1:49	2:19	2:53	3:36	4:35	6:02	9:12	12:00*
K						0:10-0:28	0:49	1:11	1:35	2:03	2:38	3:21	4:19	5:48	8:58	12:00*
J							0:10-0:31	0:54	1:19	1:47	2:20	3:04	4:02	5:40	8:40	12:00*
I								0:10-0:33	0:59	1:29	2:02	2:44	3:43	5:12	8:21	12:00*
H									0:10-0:36	1:06	1:41	2:23	3:20	4:49	7:59	12:00*
G										0:10-0:40	1:15	1:59	2:58	4:25	7:35	12:00*
F											0:10-0:45	1:29	2:28	3:57	7:05	12:00*
E												0:10-0:54	1:57	3:22	6:32	12:00*
D													0:10-1:09	2:38	5:48	12:00*
C														0:10-1:39	2:49	12:00*
B															0:10-2:10	12:00*
A																0:10-12:00*

(Rev. 1958)

INSTRUCTIONS FOR USE

Surface interval time in the table is in hours and minutes ("7:59" means 7 hours and 59 minutes). The surface interval must be at least 10 minutes.

Find the repetitive group designation letter (from the previous dive schedule) on the diagonal slope. Enter the table horizontally to select the listed surface interval time that is exactly or next greater than the actual surface interval time. The repetitive group designation for the end of the surface interval is at the head of the vertical column where the selected surface interval time is listed. For example — a previous dive was to 110 ft. for 30 minutes. The diver remains on the surface 1 hour and 30 minutes and wishes to find the new repetitive group designation: The repetitive group from the last column of the 110/30 schedule in the Standard Air Decompression Tables is "J". Enter the surface interval credit table along the horizontal line labeled "J". The 1 hour and 47 min. listed surface interval time is next greater than the actual 1 hour and 30 minutes surface interval time. Therefore, the diver has lost sufficient inert gas to place him in group "G" (at the head of the vertical column selected).

*NOTE: Dives following surface intervals of more than 12 hours are not considered repetitive dives. Actual bottom times in the Standard Air Decompression Tables may be used in computing decompression for such dives.

TABLE 1–8. REPETITIVE DIVE TIMETABLE

REPET. GROUPS	REPETITIVE DIVE DEPTH (Ft.)															
	40	50	60	70	80	90	100	110	120	130	140	150	160	170	180	190
A	7	6	5	4	4	3	3	3	3	3	2	2	2	2	2	2
B	17	13	11	9	8	7	7	6	6	6	5	5	4	4	4	4
C	25	21	17	15	13	11	10	10	9	8	7	7	6	6	6	6
D	37	29	24	20	18	16	14	13	12	11	10	9	9	8	8	8
E	49	38	30	26	23	20	18	16	15	13	12	12	11	10	10	10
F	61	47	36	31	28	24	22	20	18	16	15	14	13	13	12	11
G	73	56	44	37	32	29	26	24	21	19	18	17	16	15	14	13
H	87	66	52	43	38	33	30	27	25	22	20	19	18	17	16	15
I	101	76	61	50	43	38	34	31	28	25	23	22	20	19	18	17
J	116	87	70	57	48	43	38	34	32	28	26	24	23	22	20	19
K	138	99	79	64	54	47	43	38	35	31	29	27	26	24	22	21
L	161	111	88	72	61	53	48	42	39	35	32	30	28	26	25	24
M	187	124	97	80	68	58	52	47	43	38	35	32	31	29	27	26
N	213	142	107	87	73	64	57	51	46	40	38	35	33	31	29	28
O	241	160	117	96	80	70	62	55	50	44	40	38	36	34	31	30
Z	257	169	122	100	84	73	64	57	52	46	42	40	37	35	32	31

(Rev. 1958)

INSTRUCTIONS FOR USE

The bottom times listed in this table are called "residual nitrogen times" and are the times a diver is to consider he has already spent on bottom when he starts a repetitive dive to a specific depth. They are in minutes.

Enter the table horizontally with the repetitive group designation from the Surface Interval Credit Table. The time in each vertical column is the number of minutes that would be required (at the depth listed at the head of the column) to saturate to the particular group.

For example – the final group designation from the Surface Interval Credit Table, on the basis of a previous dive and surface interval, is "H". To plan a dive to 110 feet, determine the "residual nitrogen time" for this depth required by the repetitive group designation: Enter this table along the horizontal line labeled "H". The table shows that one must start a dive to 110 feet as though he had already been on the bottom for 27 minutes. This information can then be applied to the Standard Air Decompression table or "No Decompression" Table in a number of ways:

(1) Assuming a diver is going to finish a job and take whatever decompression is required, he must add 27 minutes to his actual bottom time and be prepared to take decompression according to the 110 foot schedules for the sum or equivalent single dive time.

(2) Assuming one wishes to make a quick inspection dive for the minimum decompression, he will decompress according to the 110/30 schedule for a dive of 3 minutes or less (27 + 3 = 30). For a dive of over 3 minutes but less than 13, he will decompress according to the 110/40 schedule (27 + 13 = 40).

(3) Assuming that one does not want to exceed the 110/50 schedule and the amount of decompression it requires, he will have to start ascent before 23 minutes of actual bottom time (50 - 27 = 23).

(4) Assuming that a diver has air for approximately 45 minutes bottom time and decompression stops, the possible dives can be computed: A dive of 13 minutes will require 23 minutes of decompression (110/40 schedule), for a total submerged time of 36 minutes. A dive of 13 to 23 minutes will require 34 minutes of decompression (110/50 schedule), for a total submerged time of 47 to 57 minutes. Therefore, to be safe, the diver will have to start ascent before 13 minutes or a standby air source will have to be provided.

TABLE 1–9. U.S. NAVY STANDARD AIR DECOMPRESSION TABLE FOR EXCEPTIONAL EXPOSURES

DEPTH (ft.)	BOTTOM TIME (Min.)	TIME TO FIRST STOP	130	120	110	100	90	80	70	60	50	40	30	20	10	TOTAL ASCENT TIME
40	360	0.5													23	24
	480	0.5													41	42
	720	0.5													69	70
60	240	0.7												2	79	82
	360	0.7												20	119	140
	480	0.7												44	148	193
	720	0.7												78	187	266
80	180	1.0												35	85	121
	240	0.8											6	52	120	179
	360	0.8											29	90	160	280
	480	0.8											59	107	187	354
	720	0.7										17	108	142	187	455
100	180	1.0										1	29	53	118	202
	240	1.0										14	42	84	142	283
	360	0.8									2	42	73	111	187	416
	480	0.8									21	61	91	142	187	502
	720	0.8									55	106	122	142	187	613
120	120	1.3										10	19	47	98	176
	180	1.2									5	27	37	76	137	283
	240	1.2									23	35	60	97	179	395
	360	1.0								18	45	64	93	142	187	550
	480	0.8							3	41	64	93	122	142	187	653
	720	0.8							32	74	100	114	122	142	187	772
140	90	1.5									2	14	18	42	88	166
	120	1.5									12	14	36	56	120	236
	180	1.3								10	26	32	54	94	168	386
	240	1.2							8	28	34	50	78	124	187	511
	360	1.0						9	32	42	64	84	122	142	187	683
	480	1.0						31	44	59	100	114	122	142	187	800
	720	0.8					16	56	88	97	100	114	122	142	187	923
170	90	1.5								12	12	14	34	52	120	232
	120	1.5						2	10	12	18	32	42	82	156	356
	180	1.3					4	10	22	28	34	50	78	120	187	535
	240	1.3					18	24	30	42	50	70	116	142	187	681
	360	1.2				22	34	40	52	60	98	114	122	142	187	873
	480	1.0			14	40	42	56	91	97	100	114	122	142	187	1006
200	5	3.2													1	5
	10	3.0													4	8
	15	2.8											1	4	10	18
	20	2.8											3	7	27	40
	25	2.8											7	14	25	49
	30	2.7										2	9	22	37	73
	40	2.5									2	8	17	23	59	112
	50	2.5									6	16	22	39	75	161
	60	2.3								2	13	17	24	51	89	199
	90	1.8					1	10	10	12	12	30	38	74	134	323
	120	1.7				6	10	10	10	24	28	40	64	98	180	472
	180	1.3		1	10	10	18	24	24	42	48	70	106	142	187	684
	240	1.3		6	20	24	24	36	42	54	68	114	122	142	187	841
	360	1.2	12	22	36	40	44	56	82	98	100	114	122	142	187	1057
210	5	3.3													1	5
	10	3.2												2	4	10
	15	3.0											1	5	13	22
	20	3.0											4	10	23	40
	25	2.8										2	7	17	27	56
	30	2.8										4	9	24	41	81
	40	2.7									4	9	19	26	63	124
	50	2.5								1	9	17	19	45	80	174
220	5	3.5													2	6
	10	3.3												2	5	11
	15	3.2											2	5	16	27
	20	3.0										1	3	11	24	43
	25	3.0										3	8	19	33	66
	30	2.8									1	7	10	23	47	91
	40	2.8									6	12	22	29	68	140
	50	2.7								3	12	17	18	51	86	190
230	5	3.7													2	6
	10	3.3											1	2	6	13
	15	3.3											3	6	18	31
	20	3.2										2	5	12	26	49
	25	3.2										4	8	22	37	75
	30	3.0									2	8	12	23	51	99
	40	2.8								1	7	15	22	34	74	156
	50	2.8								5	14	16	24	51	89	202
240	5	3.8													2	6
	10	3.5											1	3	6	14
	15	3.5											4	6	21	35
	20	3.3										3	6	15	25	53
	25	3.2									1	4	9	24	40	82
	30	3.2									4	8	15	22	56	109
	40	3.0								3	7	17	22	39	75	166
	50	2.8							1	8	15	16	29	51	94	217
250	5	3.8												1	2	7
	10	3.7											1	4	7	16
	15	3.5										1	4	7	22	38
	20	3.5										4	7	17	27	59
	25	3.3									2	7	10	24	45	92
	30	3.3									6	7	17	23	59	116
	40	3.2								5	9	17	19	45	79	178
	60	2.7					4	10	10	10	12	22	36	64	126	297
	90	2.2		8	10	10	10	10	10	28	28	44	68	98	186	518
	120															
	180							(SEE EXTREME EXPOSURES BELOW)								
	240															
260	5	4.0												1	2	7
	10	3.8											2	4	9	19
	15	3.7										2	4	10	22	42
	20	3.5									1	4	7	20	31	67
	25	3.5									3	8	11	23	50	99
	30	3.3								2	6	8	19	26	61	125
	40	3.2							1	6	11	16	19	49	84	190
270	5	4.2												1	3	9
	10	4.0											2	5	11	22
	15	3.8										3	4	11	24	46
	20	3.7									2	3	9	21	35	74
	25	3.5								2	3	8	13	23	53	106
	30	3.5								3	6	12	22	27	64	138
	40	3.3							5	6	11	17	22	51	88	204
280	5	4.3												2	3	9
	10	4.0										1	2	5	13	25
	15	3.8									1	3	4	11	26	49
	20	3.8									3	4	8	23	39	81
	25	3.7								2	5	7	16	23	56	113
	30	3.5							1	3	7	13	22	30	70	150
	40	3.3						1	6	6	13	17	27	51	93	218
290	5	4.5												2	3	10
	10	4.2										1	3	5	16	30
	15	4.0									1	3	6	12	26	52
	20	4.0									3	7	9	23	43	89
	25	3.8								3	5	8	17	23	60	120
	30	3.7							1	5	6	16	22	36	72	162
	40	3.5						3	5	7	15	16	32	51	95	264
300	5	4.7												3	8	11
	10	4.3										1	3	6	17	32
	15	4.2									2	3	6	15	26	56
	20	4.0								2	3	7	10	23	47	104
	25	3.8							1	3	6	8	19	26	61	128
	30	3.8							2	5	7	17	22	39	75	171
	40	3.7						4	6	9	15	17	34	51	90	234
	60	3.0			4	10	10	10	10	14	28	32	50	90	187	458
	90															
	120							(SEE EXTREME EXPOSURES BELOW)								
	180															

(Rev. 1958)

EXTREME EXPOSURES – 250 AND 300 FT.

DEPTH (ft.)	BOTTOM TIME (Min.)	TIME TO FIRST STOP	200	190	180	170	160	150	140	130	120	110	100	90	80	70	60	50	40	30	20	10	TOTAL ASCENT TIME
250	120	1.8							5	10	10	10	10	16	24	24	36	48	64	94	142	187	682
	180	1.5					4	8	8	10	22	24	24	32	42	44	60	84	114	122	142	187	929
	240	1.5					9	14	21	22	22	40	40	42	56	76	98	100	114	122	142	187	1107
300	90	2.3						3	8	8	10	10	10	16	24	24	34	48	64	90	142	187	691
	120	2.0				4	8	8	8	10	14	24	24	34	42	58	66	102	122	142	142	187	887
	180	1.7		6	8	8	8	14	20	21	21	28	40	40	48	56	82	98	114	122	142	187	1155

Fig. 1–32A. Repetitive Dive Worksheet (Sample for Reproduction)

REPETITIVE DIVE WORKSHEET

I. PREVIOUS DIVE:

___ minutes ⎫ see table 1-5 or 1-6 for ⎫
             ⎬   ⎬ Group___
____ feet   ⎭ repetitive group designation ⎭

II. SURFACE INTERVAL:

__hours__minutes on surface ⎫ see table 1-7 ⎫
                            ⎬   ⎬ Group___
Group___ (from I.)   ⎭ for new group ⎭

III. RESIDUAL NITROGEN TIME:

____ feet (depth of repetitive dive) ⎫ see table ⎫
                                     ⎬   ⎬ __minutes
Group___ (from II.)   ⎭ 1-8   ⎭

IV. EQUIVALENT SINGLE DIVE TIME:

___ minutes (residual nitrogen time from III.)

(add) ___ minutes (actual bottom time of repetitive dive)

(sum) ___ minutes

V. DECOMPRESSION FOR REPETITIVE DIVE:

___ minutes (equivalent single dive ⎫ see table ⎫
          time from IV.)   ⎬   ⎬
____ feet (depth of repetitive dive) ⎭ 1-5 or 1-6 ⎭

☐ No decompression required
   or
   Decompression stops:____ feet____minutes
                        ____ feet____minutes
                        ____ feet____minutes
                        ____ feet____minutes

GLOSSARY OF SKIN AND SCUBA DIVING TERMS

"AB"—abbreviation for "abalone."

ABSOLUTE PRESSURE—the addition of 14.7 lbs. (1 atmosphere) to indicated gauge pressure. True pressure.

ABSORBENT—a substance capable of taking something into itself. Rebreathers contain a chemical absorbent capable of removing CO_2 from expired breath.

ABYSMAL DEPTH—any vast depth. Prior to the invention of the Bathysphere and other modern depth-probers, this designation was given to most depths over 300 fathoms.

ADRIFT—loose from mooring or not held fast.

AIR EMBOLISM—a condition obtaining when unvented pressure due to gas expansion forces air from sacs (alveolae) in the lungs into blood vessels surrounding them. These bubbles act as dams when lodged in small vessels. Resultant lack of blood causes tissue to die.

ALVEOLAR EXCHANGE—transposition of oxygen to the blood and removal of carbon dioxide in the alveolae of the lungs.

AMBIENT PRESSURE—pressure of water (including air pressure above it) upon objects placed in it (surrounding pressure). It is usually expressed in terms of Absolute Pressure.

APPARATUS—an assembly of materials or parts designed to perform a specific operation. For example, open-circuit scuba, arbalete, rebreather.

ARTIFICIAL RESPIRATION—any means by which an alternating increase and decrease in chest volume is created, while maintaining an open airway in mouth and nose passages. Mouth-to-mouth or -nose resuscitation is now accepted as the best method.

BACKWASH—often called undertow or runout. Water piled on shore by breaking waves sets up an outward current. This is an advantage when entering from the beach.

BAR—an offshore bank or shoal forming a ridge above the bottom.

BAROTRAUMA—injury due to effects of pressure.

BLUFF BANK—a bank usually located on the convex side of a river's curve which is subject to vertical plunges due to underwater erosion. Hazardous to divers and surface craft.

BORE—a single high wave moving upstream at the mouth of a river. Caused by incoming tide opposing river current. Knowing tide tables will prevent divers from being caught by this phenomenon. Also called "eagre."

BOTTLES—hollow metal vessel "cylinders" equipped with narrow neck opening and retaining valve. Used to contain compressed breathing gases.

BREAKERS—waves broken by shore, ledge, or bar.

BREAKWATER—a structure built to break the force of waves.

BREATHING AIR—commercially prepared or machine-compressed air which is free of contaminants that would be injurious to a diver operating under pressure.

BREATHING DEVICE—an apparatus which enables divers to breathe underwater.

BUDDY BREATHING—the sharing by two or more divers of the same tank. An emergency technique used when one person's air supply is exhausted.

BUG—short for lobster.

BUOYANCY—(1) the upward force exerted upon an immersed or floating body by a fluid; (2)—neutral, positive, and negative. Neutral allows the diver to remain at a depth without effort. Positive will cause the diver to rise toward the surface, and requires effort to remain at depth. Negative results in the diver's sinking toward the bottom, and can be dangerous if not controlled.

CALM—a wind of less than one knot or one mile per hour.

CHANNEL—the deeper part of a river, harbor, or strait.

COASTAL CURRENTS—movements of water which generally parallel the shoreline. Such currents may be caused by tide or wind.

COMPRESSED-AIR DEMAND-TYPE UNITS—a breathing device using compressed air that is delivered to the diver through a regulator, as he demands it by inhalation.

CREST—maximum height of a wave.

CURRENT—a horizontal movement of water. Currents can be classified as tidal and non-tidal. Tidal currents are caused by forces of the sun and moon and are manifested in the general rise and fall occurring at regular intervals and accompanied by movement in bodies of water. Nontidal currents include the permanent currents in the general circulatory systems of the sea as well as temporary currents arising from weather conditions.

CYCLODIAL WAVES—inshore waves that are short and choppy and forceful when produced by strong winds.

CYLINDER—in diving terminology, means a compressed breathing gas container. See BOTTLES.

DARK WATER—when visibility is reduced to a minimum by material in suspension or lack of natural light. Sport divers—stay out.

DEBRIS—results of destruction or discard, wreckage, junk.

DECOMPRESSION—to release from pressure or compression.

DENSITY—the weight of anything per unit of volume.

DIAPHRAGM—a diving membrane or thin partition. The thin muscle separating the chest cavity from the abdominal cavity. The rubber (or other material) separating the demand chamber in a regulator from the surrounding water.

DISLOCATION WAVES—inaccurately called "tidal waves." Caused by underwater landslides, earthquakes, or volcanic eruption.

DIURNAL—daily rise and fall of tide.

EAGRE—see BORE.

EBB CURRENT—(1) the movement of tidal current away from shore or down a tidal stream; (2) a tide that is flowing out or causing a lower water level.

EDDY—a circular movement of water, of comparatively limited area, formed on the side of a main current. May be created at points where the mainstream passes projections or meets an opposite current.

EEL GRASS—long, thin, green strands which grow along the coast in rocky areas.

EPICENTER—the focal point of great waves.

ESTUARY—where tide meets river current. A narrow arm of the sea meeting the mouth of a river.

EXHALE—to breathe out.

EXPIRATION—the act of breathing out or emitting air from the lungs.

FACE PLATE—glass or plastic window, so constructed as to provide air space between eyes and water and to permit both eyes to see in the same plane. The skirt makes contour contact with the face, preserving air space. Pressure may be equalized by breathing into the mask. The full face plate covers eyes, nose, and mouth. The regular face plate covers eyes and nose only.

FETCH—"length of fetch" is the extent of water over which a wind blows and develops waves. The greater the distance the greater the possibility of large waves developing.

FINS—any device attached to the feet to increase area. Experimentation and ability will determine area and design best suited to the individual.

FLOTATION GEAR—any device employed to support the diver or to add additional emergency buoyancy.

FLOTSAM—wreckage of a ship or its cargo found floating on the sea.

FORCED WAVE—a wave generated and maintained by a continuous force.

FREE WAVE—a wave that continues to exist after the generating force has ceased to act.

FUNGUS—a group of simple plants that contain no chlorophyll and must therefore feed on living or dead plants or animals. The parasitic fungi are most dangerous to man.

GAUGE PRESSURE—the instrumental indication of change from normal atmospheric pressure level.

GROIN—a structure projecting from shore that is designed to break the current and thereby check erosion and build out the shore by causing a deposit of new material.

GROUND SWELL—large, usually smooth-swelling waves.

GUST—a sudden brief outburst of wind.

HALF-TIDE LEVEL—also called "mean tide level." A plane midway between mean high water and mean low water.

HEMORRHAGE—any discharge of blood from blood vessels.

HIGH WATER—the maximum height reached by a rising tide. The height may be due to periodic tidal forces alone or be augmented by weather conditions.

HOOKAH—a diving apparatus consisting of a demand regulator worn by the diver and hose connected to a compressed air supply at the surface. This is "free diving" but limited to one area by the hose length.

HURRICANE—originates over water (as do typhoons) consisting of wind rotating counterclockwise at a tremendous velocity from 75 to 100 mph. Develops in a low-pressure center and is usually accompanied by abnormally high tides. May often travel 60 mph. Diameter may range between 150 and 300 miles. Such a storm will ruin safe diving in areas covered for many days, change shoreline and bottom contours.

INHALE—the process of permitting air to enter the lungs.

INLET—a narrow strip of water running inland or between two islands.

INSPIRATION—the act of breathing in.

JETTY—a structure, as a pier, extended into a sea, lake, or river, to influence the current or tide in order to protect a harbor.

KELP—various large brown sea weeds (Laminariaceae and Fucaceae).

KNOT—velocity unit of one nautical mile (6,080.20 ft.) per hour. Equivalent to 1.689 ft. per sec. To convert ft. per sec. into knots, multiply by 0.592.

LAND BREEZE—a breeze from the direction of the land.

LANDWARD—in the direction of or being toward the land.

LEE—a sheltered place or side, that side of a ship that is farthest from the point from which the wind blows.

LEEWARD—pertaining to or in direction of, the lee side. Opposed to windward.

LEEWARD TIDE—a tide running in the same direction in which the wind blows.

LEEWAY—drifting to the leeward caused by wind or tide.

LIGHT BREEZE—a wind of 4 to 6 knots.

LIMITING ORIFICE—a hole or opening, usually of calculated size, through which the passage of a liquid or gas may be restricted within specified limits, as determined by pressure drop across the opening, to control the rate of flow.

LONGSHORE CURRENTS—movement of water close to and parallel to the shoreline.

LOW WATER—the minimum height reached by a falling tide. The height may be solely the result of periodic tidal forces or further affected by weather conditions.

MODERATE BREEZE—a wind of 11 to 16 knots (13 to 18 mph).

MODERATE GALE—a wind of 28 to 33 knots (32 to 38 mph).

NARCOSIS—a state of stupor or arrested activity.

NAUSEA—any sickness of the stomach creating a desire to vomit.

NAUTICAL MILE—also known as a geographical mile. A unit of distance designed to equal approximately 1 minute of arc of latitude. According to the national Bureau of Standards its length is 6,080.20 ft. It is approximately 1.15 times as long as the statute mile of 5,280 ft.

NEAP TIDE—a "nipped tide" or "scanty" tide which occurs near the first and third quarters of the moon; is low because of the sun and moon pulling at right angles to each other.

NONTIDAL CURRENT—current that is due to causes other than tidal forces. Classed as nontidals are the Gulf Stream, the Japan current, Labrador, and equatorial currents which are part of general ocean circulation. Also classed in this category are river discharges and temporary currents set up by winds.

NURSING—see BUDDY BREATHING.

PARTIAL PRESSURE—the effect of a gas exerting its share of the total pressure in a given volume. Air for example: Nitrogen 80% Oxygen 20% at 1 atmos. 14.7 psi. Partial press. Nitrogen = 11.76 psi; Oxygen = 2.94 psi.

PHYSICS OF DIVING—the science of matter and motion as related to man's activities underwater.

PHYSIOLOGY OF DIVING—the organic processes and phenomena dealing with life and functions of organs of human beings while in water environment.

QUICKSAND—sand that is partly held in suspension by water. Varying in depth, it easily yields to pressure of persons or objects. Resembles ordinary sand or mud and occurs on flat shores and along rivers having shifting currents.

RECOMPRESSION—returning the diver to highest pressure endured (or greater if necessary) for the purpose of minimizing and eliminating the effects of decompression sickness, air embolism. This process is accomplished in a recompression chamber rather than in return to depths.

REEF—a ridge or chain of rocks, sand, or coral occurring in or causing shallow areas.

REGULATOR—an automatic device for maintaining or adjusting the flow of air equal to the ambient pressure of the water.

RESPIRATORY MINUTE VOLUME—the amount of air inhaled and exhaled per minute to maintain proper body function. This is variable, dependent on exertion and the individual.

RIP CURRENT—a strong current of limited area flowing outward from the shore. It is usually visible as a band of agitated water in which the regular wave pattern is interrupted. This type of current is caused by the escape of water piled between shore and bar or reef by waves. The rush of escaping water is accentuated by its flow through a gap in the bar or reef. Such currents are dangerous to the uninitiated and the cause of many drownings at ocean beaches. However, when located by divers (skin and scuba) they are often used to facilitate entry to areas beyond the bar or reef.

RIPPLES—very small, gentle waves with little undulation.

RUBBER SUIT—partial or complete covering for the diver, primarily to insulate and preserve body heat. Classified as "wet" and "dry." Wet suits of foam neoprene (usually) permit a thin layer of water to contact diver's skin. Dry (rubber sheet) prevents contact with water but requires the additional insulation afforded by cloth underclothing (or wet suit).

RUNOUT—same as rip current.

RUPTURE—breaking apart, bursting—as an ear drum under unequalized pressure.

SAFETY HITCH OR BUCKLE—any fastening device that may be operated to release with one hand, easily and quickly—*a must*.

SAND BAR—a body of sand built up by action of waves or currents.

SCUBA—self-contained underwater breathing apparatus. Any free diving unit containing necessary elements to support life underwater.

SEA ANCHOR—a drag thrown overside to keep a craft headed into the wind.

SEA BOTTOM SLIDE—a landslide under water usually causing a tsunami, or dislocation wave.

SEA BREEZE—a breeze blowing over land from the sea.

SEA NEWS—rip current.

SEA PUSSES—rip current.

SEAWARD—away from land toward the open sea.

SEAWAY—one of the sea traffic lanes or routes; a vessel's headway; an area where a moderate or rough sea is running.

SEAWORTHY—fit for aquatic hazards; able to withstand usual sea conditions.

SEICHES—a geological term for "dislocation wave." See SEA BOTTOM SLIDE.

SHOAL—a place where a sea, river, etc., is shallow because of bank or bar.

SINGLE-HOSE UNIT—open-circuit scuba having a single high-pressure hose with first-stage pressure reduction at the yoke (tank attachment), second or ambient reduction at the mouthpiece. The exhaust is at the mouthpiece.

SINUS SQUEEZE—damage of tissue lining of air sinuses in the head due to failure of pressure in sinus to equalize with ambient pressure. Pain in sinuses is the signal to stop descent; rise several feet (pain diminishes). Try again cautiously. If pain persists, don't dive.

SKIN DIVING—diving without the use of scuba.

SLACK WATER—the state of a tidal current when its velocity is near zero, especially the moment when a reversing current changes direction and its velocity is zero. Occurs at high and low tide.

SNORKEL—a "J"-shaped tube, the short end of which is held in the mouth, the long end protruding above the surface, permitting breathing without raising the nose or mouth out of the water when swimming face down on the surface. Many types are available on the market, and experience will dictate which type is best for the individual.

SPEAR GUN—any device which propels a spear from a gunlike frame. Usually rubber, spring, or gas powered.

SPINDRIFT—sea spray sometimes called spoondrift; the spray and water driven from the tops of waves by wind.

SPORT DIVER—one who dives with or without scuba for game, photography, exploring, or love of the medium.

SPRING TIDES—the highest and the lowest course of tides occurring every new and full moon.

SPUME—frothy matter, foam, or scum usually collected at water line.

SQUALL—a gust of wind generally accompanied by rain or snow with nimbus clouds. Intense and of short duration.

STORM—winds of 56 to 65 knots (64 to 75 mph). Between gale and hurricane.

STRONG BREEZE—a wind of 22 to 27 knots (25 to 31 mph).

STRONG GALE—a wind of 41 to 47 knots (47 to 54 mph).

SURF—waves breaking upon a shore.

SURGE—a great rolling swell of water, a violent rising and falling.

SWELL—a large, more-or-less smooth wave.

SYMPTOMS—perceptible changes in body or function which may be indicative of disease or injury.

TANKS—a term also used to denote containers of compressed gases.

THERMOCLINE—an abrupt change in temperature encountered at varying depths.

TIDE—the periodic rise and fall of water level due to the gravitational attraction of the moon and sun acting on the earth's rotating surface.

TIDE RIP—waves and eddies in shoal water caused by tide.

TIDE WAVE—a long-period wave that has its origin in the tide-producing force and which displays itself in the rising and falling of the tide.

TOXIC—poisonous.

TROCHOIDAL WAVES—deep-water trains of waves that have great distance between crests with gentle slopes. They are the result of wind pressure, local or distant.

TROUGH—the hollow or low area between crests of waves.

TYPHOON—originates over water and consists of winds rotating in counterclockwise motion at tremendous velocity (75 to 150 mph). Develops in a low-pressure center and is accompanied by high tides. Seldom travels faster than 12 mph. Diameter may range from 150 to 300 miles.

UNDERTOW—a seaward current near the bottom of a sloping beach. It is caused by the return, under the action of gravity, of the water carried up to the shore by waves or by onshore wind.

VALVE—a device that starts, stops, or regulates the flow of gas or air in diving equipment.

VOLUME—space measured by cubic units.

WAVE—an oscillatory movement in a body of water which results in an alternate rise and fall of the surface. Maximum height is called the crest or high-water phase. The minimum height is called the trough or low-water phase. The period of a wave is the interval of time between the occurrence of successive crests at any given place. The length of a wave is the distance between two successive crests.

WAVE HEIGHT—the vertical distance from preceding trough to crest.

WHOLE GALE—wind of 48 to 55 knots (55 to 63 mph).

WINDWARD—the point or side from which the wind blows; toward the wind; in the direction from which the wind blows. Opposed to leeward.

YOKE—a device for attaching regulators to cylinders so as to make a leakproof seal. Use no more than finger pressure to attach.

INDEX